ONLY
FIFTY YEARS
AGO

ONLY
FIFTY YEARS
AGO

Gladys Hasty Carroll

LITTLE, BROWN AND COMPANY • BOSTON • TORONTO

Published simultaneously in Canada
by Little, Brown & Company (Canada) Limited

PRINTED IN THE UNITED STATES OF AMERICA

To

All the people I knew as a child

with

my love, admiration, and gratitude

AUTHOR'S NOTE

ONLY fifty years ago, had the country folk of Maine and New Hampshire been about to board an ark, they would surely have taken with them the Bible, their County Atlases and as many copies from their file of Leavitt's Almanac as they could squeeze into their carpetbags.

From its first publication, Leavitt's used year after year the same decorations to introduce each month, though below them on the page the weather prophecies, the phases of the moon and tides and the editor's advice as to how best to cooperate with nature progressed with the times. This steadfast continuity combined with an awareness of changing human needs to give its readers an invaluable sense of security. New developments continually alter the environment of the human race, yet what is known to be true remains incontrovertible forever. Thus if we but earnestly seek truth, find it and take it with us, we cannot become lost however far we travel.

It is a delight to me that the publishers have found it possible to introduce the monthly sections of this book with the Leavitt headings, which were the keynote of our months during my childhood, and also to reprint on the three pages immediately following some of the Leavitt philosophy by which our lives were influenced.

GLADYS HASTY CARROLL

LEAVITT'S
FARMER'S
ALMANACK,

IMPROVED,

AND MISCELLANEOUS YEAR BOOK,

FOR THE YEAR OF OUR LORD

1910;

BEING UNTIL JULY FOURTH, THE HUNDRED AND THIRTY-FOURTH OF AMERICAN INDEPENDENCE.

CALCULATIONS AS TO THE LATITUDE AND LONGITUDE, SO AS TO ANSWER FOR ALL THE NEW ENGLAND STATES.

Containing with the more than useful Astronomical Calculations, a larger quantity and greater variety than are to be found in any other Almanack of

MATTER, USEFUL, CURIOUS AND ENTERTAINING.

BY DUDLEY LEAVITT,

TEACHER OF MATHEMATICS AND ASTRONOMY.

CALCULATIONS BY HIS NEPHEW AND STUDENT WM. B. LEAVITT.

CALCULATIONS ACCORDING TO CLOCK TIME.

CONCORD:
EDSON C. EASTMAN.

PREFACE.

For still another time it is my honored privilege to greet my patrons, who, now increased many fold, have in innumerable pleasant ways manifested their kind appreciation of these prognostications. Under such circumstances, after long-continued favor it is indeed an honor of no humble proportions again to be permitted to address one's friends, speak one's gratitude, and welcome mutually the approach of a new year.

The twelvemonth just closed has bestowed good fortune upon some but sadly enough for the many the harvest has been ill. Wages have been reduced, storm and drought have weakened the crops, factories have shut down and with distressing incidents surrounding the movements in the stock markets it is small wonder that the country has become enveloped in a heavy cloud of depression. Yet the spirit to arise amid chaos with a firmer foundation, increased energy and a sterner ambition is truly American and ends in success as surely as day follows night. This splendid characteristic of our race was gloriously demonstrated in the trying times which succeeded the cruel panics of decades now almost forgotten. Even in this new century it has emerged triumphant from the devastation of earthquake and fire, and its effectiveness in rebuilding the prosperity of the nation in the coming year is already a glowing vista.

History reveals that reverses must be encountered periodically by all great, prosperous nations and indisputably they serve a purpose, if none better than to create incentive for more lasting accomplishments amongst those most sorely stricken. We have been told by wise philosophers on occasions without number that ability lacking opportunity is of little moment. Here in the dawn of this New Year, lies a vast opportunity and the members of our sturdy citizenship, wonderfully endowed for the test, will not be tardy in taking advantage of it.

Dudley Leavitt.

PREFACE.

To Patrons and Friends:

Once more, kind friends, we look in upon you in your goodly New England homes. Up the hill sides, across the plains, in villages and in rural shades, we find you out, and we are glad to meet so hearty a welcome.

We rejoice with you in the improvements which every year brings around. The greater facilities for diffusing intelligence, by means of books and papers, by better roads and rapid traveling, by better schools for our youth, the improved social intercourse by the grange, by the telephone in the farm houses— these are sources of a just satisfaction.

There are improvements, too, every year in accommodations for the sick by means of greater knowledge on the part of physicians, numerous hospitals and more intelligent nursing, and for the insane, the unfortunate, and for the care of children whose childhood would otherwise be neglected. These all point in the right direction, and are worthy of an enlightened and Christian people.

Then, the better construction of machinery, the improved implements of husbandry deserve a passing notice, facilitating, as they do, greater comfort in our manner of living.

But with all our new advantages, let us beware of copying anybody's extravagance. Our delights must be at home—our happiness in ourselves. Let us build our homes with virtue, and install them with competence, avoiding parade and mere show.

Meanwhile, for your continued patronage and with the wish that the new year may be a happy one, please receive the thanks of

Dudley Leavitt.

ONLY
FIFTY YEARS
AGO

YOU have heard of time tracks. Let us cross over. Cross over with me to fifty years ago in the northeast corner of the United States . . .

Here, it is the last night of the Old Year and each of us — in the Hasty with whom he identifies himself — lies in the dark below a sloping ceiling and under the weight of many comforters, or sits before an open oven door by the light of a kerosene lamp with wick turned low, listening to the clock tick, waiting for it to strike, and reviewing in these final minutes the months which have just passed.

[3]

JANUARY

JANUARY is on a blackboard covered almost entirely in white by a soft crayon of schoolhouse chalk used on its side in bold and powerful fingers. The board had been scrubbed clean, to start with, and the uncovered lines and spaces which form the crude pattern stand out glistening, three-dimensional, and move toward you, gathering you in.

The still month.

The farm lay dead in the grave to which it walked slowly every fall in thick-soled boots; slowly but calmly, like a good Christian, sure of resurrection in the spring. It always had risen, Easter after Easter. Would it yet again? The Sun-god, on which all depended, rode far away, rising and setting in a pale arc across the southern sky. Would it return? Over the farm a heavy shroud of snow was motionless. Through it ran the black line of the brook, locked in its deep, narrow channel. Around it stood the forest, in frozen garments of rusty black serge and bombazine, coarse lace and jet beads stirring

stiffly in the breath of the bitter wind and making the low moan the Irish call keening.

Hastys once lived for a generation in Ireland, on their patient way from Scotland to America. It was there that neighbors changed our name from Hastings to Hasty.

Here, in January, we have no neighbors in life, only the reflection of them across the stark expanse, by day in the woodsmoke from three sooted chimneys each spilling a dark path of ash across a white roof, by night in scattered squares of ruddy, flickering light, the nearest seeping through small panes to draw a mocking tic-tac-toe on the snow until the lamps go out. Such neighborliness as there is in winter comes with death or approaches to it. Then a man may wade waist deep to ask Verd to harness up and go for the doctor. Verd has the fastest horse for miles around. Verd goes. But Vinnie or Frankie, having ridden with him as far as the stricken, may have laid out the newborn and closed the eyelids of its mother long before the doctor comes.

The silent month.

Yet this year it brought the day of the Bells and the Black Span, and for that will always be remembered.

Within the winter confines of our small white house, our long white shed, our great dark barn, we Hastys are every day and every night intensely alive; and our creatures, our wood stoves, our meat and vegetables and fruit, our pans and tools, our very bars of yellow soap, our potted, red-blooming geraniums, the fiery frost patterns on our window glass live with us.

That morning Vinnie curled her front hair while the rest of us ate breakfast at the kitchen table. She had

eaten earlier. Frankie was doing the waiting on. Each time she opened the cellar door the heavy darkness came up from that dungeon where the narrow windows just above ground level are always buried in sawdust banking and fir branches from before the first freeze until the first green grass blade. The dark came up rich with the smell of Baldwin apples, Green Mountain potatoes in the arch, carrots and cabbages spread out on counters; pork, held down by beach stones, soaking in tubs of brine; loam in which the beets were sleeping, old cider barrels with bungholes wet from the drawing of vinegar; crocks of cucumber pickles; plum cake, hogshead cheese, and raspberry shrub in the hanging shelves; pumpkin pies, dried-apple turnovers, and molasses cookies in the stairway cupboard. All these we could have seen if we had taken a lantern into the cellar, but we did not need to see them; we knew they were there.

The dark stopped at the doorstool. The smells rushed on into the kitchen and mingled with those of oatmeal fried in salt pork fat, slabs of hot Indian bannock, boiled eggs, bowls of canned huckleberries, crust coffee; and with the singeing of Vinnie's bangs in the instant before she withdrew the curling iron and replaced it inside the chimney of her lighted hand lamp on the window sill.

The center of the room was warm by then. Not as it had been when George, the builder of this house, came from the small room which opens off the kitchen and, through the pre-dawn dusk, peered in vain into the firebox for a glowing coal from the big stick which had just started to burn there when he went to bed the night

before. He had built a new fire with chips and edgings
and oil from a bottle with a quill in the cork, broken
ice in the water pail to fill the teakettle, and gone to
the shed to work at the chopping block and the saw-
horse until Verd came down with the milk pails. Now
the milk had come in and been strained through cheesecloth and set away in shallow pans for the cream to rise
for the butter-making, Hal and Marcy by turns had
dressed in the shelter of the open oven door, and the
center of the room was warm. Vinnie stood on the peri-
meter of the circle of warmth, curling her hair.

Vinnie is not beautiful as Frankie is, but she is taller
and looks stronger. So George saw his daughter that
morning, glancing out of steel-gray eyes deep-set under
shaggy dark eyebrows and above crisp pepper-and-salt
mustache and muttonchop whiskers. Tall and strong
with a light foot for a woman of her size, never rattled
the dishes in the cupboard when she crossed the floor;
best hand with biscuit and pie dough anywhere around
now, had her mother's knack; had filled her mother's
place with him as much as a daughter could since she
was fifteen; made his shirts, knit his socks, patched his
mittens, washed his clothes, rubbed his back, slept right
there in the parlor where she could hear him if he was
took in the night. George hoped she would live as long
as he did, drained his glass of well water — his only
drink the year around — and wiped his mouth with the
back of his hand.

But Vinnie is more than that. Else why does she curl
her hair?

To Hal she was the one above all others who must be

and most readily was accorded respect. He supposed she curled her hair because a teacher ought to have curly hair; that a woman like his mother who rarely left her house except to attend the sick and dying and never without a hat was decent in a smooth pompadour, tortoiseshell pins, and side and back combs with brilliants; but a woman who sat all day behind a desk in command of twenty-seven pupils and who might at any hour hear the rap of a school committeeman at the door must be curled. Whatever Aunt Vinnie did was right. Everybody knew that. She always got the same answers as were printed in the back of the book. There was no word she could not spell. She could find capitals and trace rivers and point out mountain ranges on a map with her eyes shut. He had himself read in the Town Report where it said, "Miss Vinnie V. Hasty, though young, is an excellent disciplinarian, and her pupils in general are making good progress," and "We are fortunate in having in District Number 11 the services of Miss Vinnie V. Hasty, a teacher of considerable talent for the discipline of the young, the inspiration of their minds, and the moulding of their characters." She was the superintendent of the summer Sunday School. Even at home his grandfather said the food she cooked was the best, his father had her check his figures every Saturday night, his mother always asked her about the sewing — whether the armscye was too big, if enough had been allowed for the seams, how deep the hem should be — and she was the only one who could get Marcy off her wild horses without making her cry.

Miss Vinnie . . . Miss Vinnie V. . . .

Verd did not look at her at all that morning. He hardly ever looked at Vinnie. And Frankie knew the reasons why.

One of the reasons she carried with her always, and gladly, like a love letter pinned to her corset and concealed by the loose folds of her calico wrapper. Though Verd had been married to her more than fifteen years, none of them easy, and she had borne him two children, whenever he was in the house he was watching Frankie, charmed by the luster in her wide violet eyes and blue-black hair, the proud carriage of her head on a slender neck, the translucent whiteness of her skin, the sloping shoulders, her waist which he could still enclose with his two hands, her narrow wrists and ankles, her long white fingers . . . *Pale hands I love* . . .

But the other reason, which for two years Frankie had been pushing down, determined to smother, resolved to deny or at least to forget, was unaccountably leaping in her heart that morning, hot, searing as acid in the throat. For Frankie thought with her heart.

Verd did not look at his sister because he was ashamed. Not of her but of himself. And all because he had done what he believed was right; done this without hesitation, at great sacrifice to himself and to Frankie, and in secret so that only Frankie knew what he had done; and they received no credit for it, never would, nor wanted any. All they wanted was that it should have been right, as they had taken for granted at the time it was, and as for a long time now they had both been quite sure it wasn't, but never spoke of it even to each other in the night. For two who knew what love between a man and a women was it did not bear thinking on, much less speaking of.

Still, Frankie too often thought of it, and so did Verd. They were thinking of it that January morning as Vinnie, in her brown challis school dress with the green velvet yoke and cuffs and ruffles around the full skirt, curled her hair by the back window and looked across the white fields at dark hills covered with dark trees like standing swords, blade-sharp and point-sharp.

Two years before, Verd and his family had been living in half a house with bay windows in a small city twenty miles from here. Marcy had been born there. Hal was in school there. Verd was earning good pay working for a carriage and sign painter, and the Hupmobiles, Maxwells, Oaklands belonging to doctors and lawyers, as well as the Stanley Steamers elegant old ladies drove along the streets, were coming in for fresh coats of paint and fancy striping. The woman who owned the house in which they lived, and who lived in the other side of it, was a dressmaker, and Frankie worked with her a part of every day. There was a corner grocery near enough so that Frankie could go to it without being out of sight of her bay windows. Every night at dusk the lamplighter came to touch off the gas inside shades which seemed to float in the dark like white balloons. Frankie took the children to church every Sunday morning the year around, and they heard the bells chime, the pipe organ play, the white-robed choir sing.

Here George and Vinnie had been alone, and content enough so, until a few months earlier. Then the thought had come to George that the new sawyer at Earle's mill at the end of the road was likely not used to living out the winter in a tar-paper shanty like the French wood-choppers. Fon Drew had the ways of a man used to better, likely would be glad of a clean featherbed in a plastered chamber of nights and Vinnie's cooking three times a day, and might pay what it was worth to him. George has ever had a sharp eye out for an extra dollar, and he likes to have a man around to speak to, too. He had mentioned this to Vinnie, and Vinnie answered that one more to clean up after would be no trouble to speak of; she could pack three lunches almost as quickly as two before she went to school, and what was an extra plate and cup and saucer?

So Fon Drew had come and was still there when Verd came home the next summer to help George with the haying. Since Verd brought his family there was no room for Fon to sleep at the house, so he went nights to his shanty but was back for meals and usually spent the evenings unless he and Vinnie went for a ride or a walk and perhaps called on a neighbor who had a grapho-phone. One night they went to a serenade. Fon was good company. They all liked him.

But late that fall a neighbor had driven five miles and paid to ride fifteen on the train to see Verd at the paint shop. He talked for a few minutes about the horseless buggy with brass lamps, and about the name CHARLES M. SWEET, M.D. which Verd was gold-leafing on the door; he squeezed the rubber bulb to make the horn sound, and laughed, said he had been wanting to do that ever since he first heard one squawk. But then he called Verd outside, where they could not be

heard — the wind was raw that day — and told him he
and Frankie had better close out here and come home;
that George and Vinnie probably didn't know it, but talk
had started about Fon Drew and Vinnie, his living there
the way he did. Of course the neighbors knew Vinnie
would never do anything wrong, but Verd must see it
didn't look right and nobody could say it did when folks
in the village spoke of it. Unless something was done
quick to stop the talk, the upshot of it might be that
Vinnie would lose the school and her reputation into the
bargain.

This neighbor had been a good friend to George and
Verd all their lives. He had a two-horse team and came
to plow for us every spring; this took all day and Vinnie
cooked a boiled dinner for him; in exchange George or
Verd had always held plow for him on his land, and ate
with relish his wife's chicken pie and tapioca pudding
with sliced bananas in it and mounds of white of egg
on top. He said he was sorry to bring bad tidings, Verd
thanked him for his trouble, and he took his slow way
home. It made a full day's trip for him, and the time
not begrudged.

Verd went back to the house with the bay windows
that night and told Frankie what he had heard. Within
three days their furniture was stored and they had gone
home. No other course was possible. Yet the reason why
could never be given to anyone, least of all to Vinnie or
her father.

The reason they gave was that Verd wanted to build
a paint shop and have his own business; but this was
late fall and he could not put in a foundation until

spring. Frankie said she did not feel Hal's schooling had been as good as he would get with Vinnie; but this was a hard season to leave a school around the corner of a city street and break in at one two miles up a country road. Why had they come, with no warning, before Christmas? The question was never asked nor answered.

Verd and Frankie took over the east chamber, which had always been Verd's and where they had spent their wedding night. The only place for Hal to sleep was in the west chamber, which had been the guest room before it was Fon's. Marcy had the windowless alcove at the head of the back stairs. Fon, an odd expression on his face, put his few possessions into a carpetbag and went back to his shanty. Verd drove him over there and took along dry wood and built a fire in the rusty stove before he left. Verd tried to make conversation, too, about the price of lumber by the thousand, and how much work was on hand now at the mill. But Fon answered shortly, and none of us saw him again. A few days later the mill was shut down until a new sawyer could be found. Fon had gone in the night, leaving no message.

When George heard of this and expressed his surprise at the supper table, Vinnie said, "I don't see why everybody is so surprised. The children were talking about it at school today and I told them it was a wonder to me he stayed as long as he did. From things he said here, I took it he never had before, anywhere."

"He told me last summer if I was ever here long enough, he and I would make me a birchbark canoe," Hal said. "Now I'm here, and he's gone."

"I guess next summer your father can help you build

a canoe," Vinnie told him. "I don't know about that much birchbark, these days. Couldn't you use canvas?"

There was nothing in Vinnie's words, voice, or face to indicate that whether Fon Drew came or whether he went was of more than passing interest to her. But it stood to reason.

How did a healthy young woman live without a man of her own to love and be loved by, and with only other people's children to button up and teach and scold and cuddle? Sleeping alone in a big brass bed between the organ and the marble-topped table, among the red plush chairs, rockers, and love seat bought with the money she had earned! All her married life Frankie had been sorry for Vinnie, as one after another of her schoolmates and then of her oldest girl pupils found their men and made their sheets and took their vows; and still there was no man for Vinnie.

That morning in January, Frankie ached with pity and burned with remorse.

Because at last there had come one. A man as tall as Vinnie, as old as Vinnie, as unmarried as Vinnie, as well educated as Vinnie. A proud and merry man with narrow brown eyes, a small black mustache, a way of making fun which amused everyone and offended no one . . . But he had been driven away. Verd and Frankie themselves had driven him away. And now, two years afterward, Vinnie stood alone, at the edge of warmth, by her father's back window, curling her hair . . .

Marcy was staring at Vinnie, forgetting to eat. How exciting her hair was, in tight, bouncing little curls full of red and gold lights! How tall and straight she stood,

like a queen! How white her ear was! How sweetly
her dress swirled around her! How rich the velvet at
her throat, and how bright the gold beads which lay
against it! Sixty gold beads. Marcy had counted them
all many times.

"Some day," thought Marcy. "Some day *I* — "

The snow which had been loose and soft in a sudden
January thaw had as suddenly frozen hard last night
and would not melt at all that day, for the mercury
was still at nine below and the wind was from the north.
It was a day for going deep into the woods to chop cord-
wood and haul it home. George went out of the yard
first, on the seat of the horse-sleds, the collar of his sheep-
skin-lined coat turned up around his ears, the moisture
of his breath hanging in icicles from his whiskers, and
Vinnie riding with him as far as the schoolhouse in her
glossy black caracul coat, her brown velvet hat with the
pink velvet rose under the rim, a sheer black scarf tied
under her round, cleft chin, black velvet boots with fur
tops, and black wool lace mittens. Verd followed a few
minutes later, but had Hal at the schoolhouse in time
to build the fire before Vinnie got there, for Bess, Verd's
horse, is Old Bell's daughter, never more than half
broken to harness, and fleet as a deer.

It was too cold to wash and hang out clothes, but it
was Monday, and on Mondays Frankie washed. Verd had
brought in the copper boiler and the wooden bench and
tubs from the shed, and Hal had filled them with water
from the well.

"At school," thought Marcy, "everybody knows the
multiplication tables all the way to twelve times twelve,

can read fine print and spell long words, knows all the states and capitals and counties . . . Androscoggin, Aroostook, Cumberland, Franklin, Hancock, Kennebec, Knox . . .'' It was still a long way down to her own county, York. She got her slate, sat on the end of the kitchen couch, and began to print.

Frankie was singing at her work in a brave attempt to brighten the dark corners of her heart. Marcy cannot sing, but her mother can. Sometimes when Frankie sings, Marcy hides in a closet and cries, not only because it is so beautiful to hear but because it tells her that a time will come when she cannot hear her mother singing.

That day Frankie called Marcy from her writing to dry the dishes, and tried to teach her ''Hold the Fort,'' but as usual the notes did not come out right, and when both began to be discouraged Frankie asked her what time it was. Marcy went and stood, head tipped back, concentrating on the clock face, the half of an unbleached sugar bag which was her dish towel trailing on the floor.

''Ten,'' Marcy said. ''Ten minutes past nine . . . Almost.''

''That's *right*,'' cried Frankie. ''Here's a dry towel.''

''Auntie is bewitched,'' said Marcy.

''She's — *what*?''

''Bewitched . . . I don't think I mean bewitched . . . I mean enchanted. Like the Sleeping Beauty and Rapunzel and Snow White. That she reads to me about.''

''How — like them?''

''Just is.''

''What made you think of her when you were looking at the clock?''

"I think about her all the time. I wonder how she got — enchanted. Who did it. I think somebody has to do it. I want to be enchanted, too. Just like her."

"Oh, Marcy, you — you — "

Sometimes Marcy frightens Frankie.

"I'm going to ask her tonight who enchanted her. I wonder if she knows. Maybe you don't know when it happens. Maybe I'm enchanted now."

Though it was a January Monday like other January Mondays, there were these little differences to be remembered now. Vinnie curled her hair that morning instead of the day before. Verd went into the woods with his father instead of to his paint shop in town. Marcy talked glibly of enchantment. The clothes froze as they were put on the line, and hung there all day like torn effigies or broken statues. A lamp chimney Frankie was drying came apart in her hands. By three o'clock in the afternoon black clouds had covered the pale sky and the pale sun, and it was growing dark so fast that George and Verd started out of the woods an hour early. The temperature had not risen to zero, and where the horses broke through the crust they cut their feet and left red blotches on the snow. The men thought to find Vinnie and Hal at the schoolhouse and bring them home. But the building was locked. Verd picked up Hal on the road.

For by then it had happened. The kettle which had been simmering all day had boiled over. The bells had rung.

Marcy was the first to hear them. She was reading a story to her mother from the back cover of the *New*

England Homestead, where the print was so fine that no one would know without looking very hard that she was not reading but making up the story as she went along.

Pausing and cocking her head, she said, "I hear bells."

"Anybody making a horse drag a sleigh over rough traveling like this wants to go pretty bad," Frankie said.

They went to the window. By then they knew it was not a few brass bells jangling on the shafts of a sleigh. It was silver bells, set close together on a leather strap girdling a lively horse, for they did not jangle; they sang and danced. And as Frankie and Marcy watched the turn of the road by the bridge they saw that it was not one horse but two. A black span of racing horses, with two girdles of bells, and bells on the third shaft between them, too, flying over the snow, while clouds of breath steamed from their nostrils, drawing behind them as if it were a toy a brilliant red cutter with brass railings gleaming in the sun, and a great black fur robe — "Bearskin," thought Frankie — and above the robe a man's arms pulled out straight by the power of the horses, and a man's head in a shiny black derby hat.

It all flashed by the end of the lane and disappeared, but Frankie and Marcy both saw it. They saw it plain and clear, and have never forgotten it. They stayed by the window until they could no longer hear the bells.

Then Frankie asked faintly, expecting no answer, "Now who in the dear Lord's world — was that?"

But Marcy always had an answer.

"Some prince," said Marcy calmly. "Some prince or

other. Some eldest son. I think he has come for Auntie. He will give her a kiss.''

She went back to cutting paper dolls from the mail-order catalogue, humming tunelessly as she worked the scissors in and out around the plumes and the ruffles and the pointed toes. Then the black clouds came; the sunlight sputtered and went out like a lamp turned too low. Marcy went to lean against her mother, who had dropped into a rocker by the window.

And then the bells again. The chiming, silver bells and the racing feet of the black span. Two white, flying lamps throwing two white lines across the night like twin paths of mother-of-pearl, and a little behind them one huge, glowing ruby. And as suddenly there was nothing to see. The singing, dancing sound died away and was gone.

''That was Aladdin's lamp,'' said Marcy. ''I saw him rub it. Against the black fur robe. Then he went up into the air. Straight up. Like a genie.''

''Oh, Marcy,'' Frankie cried, *''hold your tongue!''*

Marcy, offended, withdrew with great dignity into the dark. ''I am blind,'' she thought, ''and alone. But I shall find refuge. Because I must.'' She spread her arms like wings, this small, unseen, and unseeing angel, found the couch, and sat on it without movement, almost without breathing. Let her mother think she had flown away.

''Mama!'' Hal called loudly, opening the door.

''What is it? What's the matter?'' Frankie rose stiffly and struck a match. *Dear Lord, what next?*

"Nothing, I guess." You could hear the relief in his voice. "We didn't know but what there was, coming up the lane. House dark as a pocket."

"Where's Vinnie?"

"Wait till you hear!" He sounded pleased.

The heat of the match flame reached the tips of Frankie's fingers and she had to let it fall to the top of the stove. But she had strength now to strike another and to light the lamp on the table. Hal pulled off his mittens and was unbuckling his boots.

"Where is she, Hal?"

"Gone to an oyster supper at the village! With Fon Drew! In a rig from the livery stable. Two black horses and a red cutter. Papa says he painted that cutter. It was all fancy with black and gold striping. Fon drove right up into the schoolyard and you can bet nobody near a window kept their eyes on their books. He couldn't hitch. No post there stout enough to hold that span! So she had to go to the door to speak to him. After a minute she came back and dismissed school; said so everybody could get home before dark. Told me to shut the stove up and lock the door before I left. Then she climbed into the cutter and he held that span *with one hand* while he fixed a great black fur robe around her with the other. Then he grinned down at me and says, 'I'll see you again, Butch. Tell your folks I've taken your Aunt Vinnie to an oyster supper in the village. It's in a church vestry, tell them. There's a hayride afterwards but we won't go on that. If she lived out in Oregon we would, but it would be too risky for a Maine school-

teacher. Tell your folks she'll be home by nine o'clock.'
And off they went, bells ringing and snowballs flying out
from under the feet of that black span.''

Verd had come in for the milk pails and stood listening, though he had heard it all before on the way down
the road.

''Well,'' Frankie said to Hal, as calmly as she could,
''I guess she'll have a great time, won't she?''

''Ought to,'' Hal answered. ''In such a rig as that.
I just hope, now he's back, he'll stay around to be here
next summer and show me how to make a birchbark
canoe.''

Frankie went into the sinkroom to get down the milk
pails, and Verd followed her.

''I feel as if I'd been a prisoner at the dock,'' he
whispered, ''and the jury brought in a verdict of not
guilty.''

''I know,'' Frankie whispered back. ''She's got her
chance again. I don't know what'll come of it. But glad
and thankful am I she took it.''

He pulled her against him and kissed the back of her
neck, thinking no one was looking. But Marcy was always looking.

As soon as he left she asked, ''Can I stay up, Mama?
Can I stay up till she comes?''

''We'll see. Not if it's as late as nine o'clock. We'll
all be abed and asleep.''

But the kitchen left neat, with a lamp burning, a good
fire in the stove, tea steeping, and cookies on the table
in a company plate . . .

In the barn, above the drone of warm milk spraying

into the pails between their knees, Verd told George where Vinnie was.

"That so?" George said. "Where's Fon been to, so long?"

"Out in Oregon, I take it."

"Guess he's quite a rolling stone."

"Must have gathered some moss, though, to come back and hire that stable rig."

"If he has, hiring that rig is wearing of it off . . . Well, takes all kinds. Prob'ly got him some good yarns to spin, out there. Hope he stays around long enough for us to hear 'em. Nice talker, Fon is. Always was."

If it occurred to George, his forehead pressed against the smooth flank of his best Jersey cow, that Vinnie might join Fon Drew in his rolling, and so would not be here to make her father's shirts, patch his mittens, and sleep in the next room where she could hear him if he called her in the night, he gave no sign of it.

Supper was a little late, but good enough when it was put on the table. We drew up our chairs, looked at Vinnie's vacant place, and spoke of how she was feasting on oyster stew.

Marcy had never eaten oysters. She supposed they were a kind of ambrosia. She liked the word *ambrosia* better. She wondered how it was spelled. Am-bro-si-a . . .

There was a circle of light around the lamp which took in the table, our hands, and our faces. The circle of warmth from the stove, having widened since morning, enclosed all these and the whole room except its corners. This larger circle was walled in like a birthday cake with one candle by the square box which is our house.

Above and all around this small, square, white-painted wooden box hung the cold black curtains of a starless night in the Still Month. Below it the frozen farm lay in its icy shroud. And the only sound on the dark face of the earth was the low moan the Irish call keening.

FEBRUARY

FEBRUARY is the uncertain month, neither black nor white but all shades between by turns. Nothing is sure. The woods pond, where ice was cut in two-foot blocks and hauled away last month, is still frozen over but now would not support a horse; a man crossing it with his gun under his arm, thinking of rabbit stew, may disappear beneath the ice in a twinkling and his body not be found until it surfaces in the spring. The snow of the fields drags down on the feet like quicksand. A woman stoops low to take potatoes from the cellar bin. Will they last until a new crop grows, or even sets on? Will seed potatoes sprout and send up shoots to bloom again, as other years they have? Each year is new and strange in February. Its promises, if any, are like shadow pictures on the wall; one cannot grasp and hold to them; blow out the light and they are no longer there.

One evening early that month Fon Drew came to our house as he had several times in the past two weeks. After the first time he rode up with Verd from the paint shop, and unless Verd took him back after supper, the man who kept the boardinghouse where Fon was staying would drive up for him about our bedtime, which is between eight and nine o'clock. Twice he and Vinnie, on a warm night for the season, walked a mile or so to call on neighbors Fon had known when he worked at the sawmill, and listened to graphophone records. One night, during a cold stretch, they had gone skating on the river, carrying small lanterns to light their way. But Fon was a great talker, would far rather spin yarns than listen to records or skate; so most of the times he came he sat long at the supper table and talked, then moved back to the chair at the end of the stove, lit his pipe, and talked until it was time to go.

It was the same that February night, only he had hired the boardinghouse keeper's horse and pung and so could choose his own time for leaving. And that night he brought presents. A copy of a magazine, *Popular Mechanics,* which he said would come every month to Hal. Rocks with streaks of gold in them from California for George and Verd. A lump of hard coal, all shining blue and purple, from Pennsylvania for Frankie; Fon said, flashing his white smile, that it was the color of her eyes. Chocolate creams and marzipan for Vinnie, rows and rows of them, each candy in its own pink paper cup, all enfolded in gold paper lace and with gold tongs like sugar tongs to lift them with ... And for Marcy a small metal trunk with leather straps and gilt buckles. When she opened it, she found a baby doll with a wax face and a cloth body, wearing a bonnet and a long white dress and wrapped in a white shawl with fringe.

While Fon told new stories — his supply seemed to have no end — of logging camps, river drives, mines, bears, and wolves, Hal sat by the lamp with his magazine open on the table, but he was not reading. Frankie and Vinnie rocked gently, each at her own end of the dropleaf table between the back windows, one knitting, the other darning. George lay on the couch with his boots under its side and the County Atlas under the head of it. This atlas is George's favorite book, but on the wall shelves above him he keeps his well-worn town reports and Leavitt's Almanacs for several years back. The slim, bound volumes of local tales by Dr. Jewett's daughter are there only because they were his wife's. George wastes neither time nor eyesight on what a woman made up out of her own head. Fon's stories, now, had substance. Fon had seen and done these things he told of, or knew flesh-and-blood men who had.

Verd sat in one of the two straight chairs at the foot of the couch with his arm across the back of the other, in which Marcy was curled, leaning against him, staring in shy wonder at the baby doll, and half-hearing the great, rolling words in Fon's deep, rich voice which mingled with the puffs of smoke from his pipe and drifted through the room, cloud on cloud, until the walls disappeared, and the clock, and the furniture, and the faces, and there was nothing anywhere but Words . . .

The next thing Marcy knew, it was morning.

She opened her eyes, and though it was hardly light, she sensed instantly that she was the only one in the house still abed. She slipped out of her cot in the windowless alcove and ran barefoot into Hal's room. He

was not there. Shivering in the gray chill, she struggled
to force on the red felt slippers which were too small, and
padded down the back stairs.

As soon as she opened the kitchen door, though the
room was full of people, the feeling with which she had
wakened — a feeling of emptiness — grew. It was a feeling like the silence when the clock stops ticking, but much
bigger. It was hard to breathe, as when in the night you
have pulled the comforter over your face to warm your
nose and you have to push the comforter away. But she
could not push it away.

Her Uncle Clarence sat on the foot of the couch looking straight ahead but not seeing anything. It was
strange to see him like that. It was strange to see him
at all in the winter.

Clarence Hasty is the son of George's brother Joseph,
and so the cousin of Verd and Vinnie. He is also the
husband of Frankie's younger sister Lula, and the father
of Marcy's cousin, the baby Ruth. He is a handsome
man, tall and lean, with deep-set dark eyes and strong
hands, and he plays the violin. But that morning his eyes
did not see what they looked at and his hands lay stiff
on his knees as if they were no part of him.

Hal sat beside him, not touching him, like a small
copy of Clarence, as if he felt whatever Clarence felt
without knowing what it was. There has always been a
bond between these two. Clarence taught Hal to swim
and to shoot and in the fall they go into the woods together to take a share of honey from the hives of wild
bees.

George and Verd were at the table, eating rapidly, but

the food looked strange. There had been no time to heat it. It had come directly to the table from the cupboard. Only now the tea had steeped, and Vinnie was pouring it into big cups. She stirred milk and sugar into one, and pulled out a chair at the table.

"Sit up and warm your stomach, Clarence. Come."

But he did not come, and she carried the cup to him in both hands as if it were a bowl. He looked up at her as if he did not know her, and took a swallow like a child. But only one.

Frankie was in the sinkroom, crying.

Eating and crying and staring. And emptiness all around. Marcy in the tight red felt slippers and long, ruffled red flannel nightgown felt invisible.

Verd stood up and reached for his coat and cap.

"I'll harness and take you down to the village," he said.

George turned his head toward the sinkroom.

"I callate you'll want to go up there," he said. "I'll take you and Vinnie and Hal at the same time. Rig up warm. Damp out."

Frankie hurried through the kitchen and upstairs.

Everybody was going somewhere. Everybody but Marcy.

"Marcy can't stay alone," said Vinnie. "I'd take her with me but for her cold. I guess you'll have to stay home today, Hal. Father, I'd better get your great-coat and your good cap with the earlappers for Clarence. He's not rigged for riding."

"Go ahead," George grunted, pulling on his boots. "Git 'em."

Marcy watched Verd and Clarence go out of the yard behind Bess, and George come out of the barn with Old Bell and the pung. George never used the pung except on Friday, which was market day, when he took eggs and butter and vegetables to his customers in the village. But he was using it today and this was Tuesday.

Vinnie came out of the parlor, dressed for school as usual, and picked up her books and lunchbox.

"Keep the fire going, Hal, but don't let it get too hot. If you warm up anything in the spider, watch the fat."

Frankie came down from upstairs, wearing her best hat and black caracul coat and carrying a big bundle. Her eyes were red-rimmed and her face was swollen, but she had stopped crying.

She almost passed Marcy, then stopped and pulled the child against her with her free arm. The caracul coat smelled of cloves from the pomander ball which had hung inside it in the closet.

"Oh, Marcy, Marcy," she whispered. "Get dressed and stay where it's warm."

She was beginning to cry again, and when she rode out of the yard beside Vinnie on the back seat of the pung her face was hidden in her handkerchief.

When she and Hal were alone, Marcy spoke for the first time that day.

"Why was Mama crying?"

"Because — little Ruth is dead."

"Aunt Lula's baby."

"Yes. Uncle Clarence's too."

"And Grammy's."

"Yes."

"I didn't know that baby very well. Grammy was always holding her."

"Because she was sick. She was sick a long time."

"They used to give her medicine."

"They were trying to make her well. But they couldn't."

"I don't think," said Marcy, "that medicine is *good* for people. At *all*."

"Don't be silly. I used to have to take a lot of medicine. I had convulsions. If I hadn't taken medicine I would have died."

"They're always talking about that. They say it tasted awful, and you used to ask them, 'Isn't it time for my asafetida?' *I* think it was that old asafetida *made* you have convulsions."

Marcy's lips were twisting into a smile. She felt strangely triumphant. They all thought medicine was good for you, but she knew it was bad, so when they tried to give it to her she kicked and screamed, and if they held her hands and feet and nose and put it in her mouth she tried not to swallow, but held her breath until they were frightened and let her go. Then she spat it out or threw it up. So she was alive and had never had a convulsion.

But she also knew she should not smile today, and was glad when Hal said, "Oh, you're always thinking and saying things you don't know anything about," because that made her angry and stopped her smiling. If she could get angry enough and stay angry, it would fill the emptiness. To do this it became necessary for her to develop anger at sadness, because for the next three days sadness was what surrounded her like a fog.

George came back with a suitcase. Marcy opened it and found it full of black cloth and patterns. Her mother had put in a letter for Vinnie but it was sealed, and Hal told Marcy anybody could be sent to prison for breaking the seal of a letter addressed to someone else.

Verd and Clarence came back, and Clarence sat in the middle of the kitchen floor with one of Frankie's calico aprons over his shoulders while Verd cut his hair. Neither man spoke. Hal put dinner on the table, trying to step quietly in his thick-soled shoes, but nobody ate much. The fried potatoes had stuck to the spider and burned black, and the steamed biscuits were wet on the bottom. Nobody said anything. Verd and Clarence rode away. When Verd came back he brought Vinnie with him. She read Frankie's letter.

"Well," she said, "the ironing won't get done to-night." When Frankie was here, she always ironed on Tuesday morning. "I have to make a dress for your Aunt Lula. Your mother is making over a coat to fit her. She didn't have any black clothes."

"Does Grammy?"

"All your grandmother's best clothes are black. But the only silk gloves she has are worn out, your mother says."

"Can she wear somebody else's?"

"Nobody else old enough to have black silk gloves has hands as small as your grandmother's. Her hands are no bigger than yours."

Marcy looked at her hands. Some day she would be

old enough for black silk gloves and she would have to wear them because somebody died?

Supper was soon over, and the thick cloth spread to show dark gray through pale tissue paper. Hal held the lamp high while Vinnie's scissors went in and out. The bright throw disappeared from the sewing machine and Vinnie bent low to thread its needle, then fed the cloth in, her feet busy on the treadle which made the wheel turn. Stitch, stitch, stitch; fastening dark to dark. George lay on the couch in the shadows, too far from the lamp for anyone to see whether he breathed. Marcy wanted to sit beside him, to lean against his chest and feel it go in and out, but she did not dare, for fear it might not; her grandfather was old. She thought of the night before, of Fon and his voice, the candy in the pink paper and gold lace, the doll. She opened the trunk and looked at the doll as she had several times that day, but she had not touched it. It looked to her like Grammy's baby Ruth.

"Want a piece of candy, Marcy?" Vinnie asked as she stopped stitching to turn the cloth.

Marcy shook her head. She wished Fon would come now. She needed him. They all needed him. She wished he would come and stay and fill the house with big, rolling words and make the world all new, a place of pink paper and gold lace where you could lift out with little gold tongs whatever you wanted and nothing you did not want.

Verd went into the sinkroom and washed and drank from the dipper.

When he came back he put his hand on Marcy's head

and said, "That's quite a doll you've got there."

Marcy did not answer, but she liked the heavy warmth of her father's hand.

"How's your cold tonight?"

"Better."

"You'd better go to bed now. You go to bed and get over your cold and I'll take you down to the shop with me tomorrow. So Hal can go to school."

Marcy had been to the paint shop with Verd twice in the summer, riding there behind Bess in the red gig, a ride better than those on roller coasters at the Fairground, where Marcy has never been. Then she had played in the yard among the bright finished wagons and carts pushed out into the sun, ready for delivery. Verd had given her a can of paint and a brush and a board on which to copy the letters of a sign he had just made. They had eaten their lunch sitting on a bench in the wide open shop door, and people driving by waved their whips in greeting if they did not turn in to talk. Once, after lunch, they had gone into a meadow to pick wild strawberries for Marcy to take home to her mother. The other time, after lunch, they climbed Powderhouse Hill, and it was so clear a day that Marcy could see what her father said was snow on Mount Washington.

But that was June and August. This was February. The sky was gray, the snow was gray, the air was damp. Marcy sat listlessly on a chair beside the little stove, holding a sample book in her lap, watching her father's steady hand striping the doctor's car, a narrow stripe of gold around the door, a narrower stripe of red on either side of the gold, and the doctor's initials in gold above the handle. Last night was the first that she had not slept under the same roof with her mother. Always before she had liked the smell of paint. Now it made her feel queer, and she remembered that when she was pressed up, her mother rubbed her chest with melted lard and turpentine and covered it with hot flannel.

"I probably ought not to have brought her out," Verd thought. "She sits there humped up like a sick kitten."

He laid the back of his hand against her forehead. It felt hot, but that might be from the stove.

He began wiping his brushes and pouring turpentine on his hands to clean them.

"Guess we'd better knock off for the day," he said. "Have to go downtown for a few things."

The buildings came closer and closer together as if for shelter against the cold and damp. They were like sheep huddling. When they were all one long wall of brick with signs which Verd had lettered and decorated, he began pulling in hard on the reins.

"I've got to go down here quite a ways, so I'm going to let you off to do an errand for your mother. She wants a pair of black silk gloves for your grandmother. Size five. You go in right under that sign that says DRY GOODS & FANCY NOTIONS. Tell the lady you want a pair of black silk gloves, size five. Can you remember that?"

Marcy nodded.

"Ask her if they're not right can you bring them back. Here's a dollar. And wait inside the door until you see me pull up in front. Get warmed up for the ride home."

He stopped and Marcy climbed down. He tried to wait until she reached the door, but Bess would not stand. Marcy watched them disappear along the brick wall. She was alone. In the village, alone, holding a piece of green paper.

She looked up at the sign, DRY GOODS & FANCY NOTIONS. She pushed open the door. It was heavy, and she had to push hard.

Inside, it was so dark that at first she could see nothing. Dark and silent. She stood still, blinking. Then she began to see the outline of a long, wide, bare counter beside her, and behind it shelves filled from floor to ceiling with white boxes. A small woman with a sharp nose and sharp chin was coming toward her out of the dark.

"Shut that door! Can't heat the whole face of the earth!"

In anxious terror, Marcy closed the door. The woman waited. Marcy looked at the toes of her boots.

"Well, what do you want?"

"A pair . . . of black silk . . . gloves . . . size five, and —"

"Speak up child. I can't hear you."

"A pair . . . of black silk . . . gloves . . . size five . . . and if-they're-not-right-can-I-bring-them back?"

The woman pulled a box from a shelf. It made a rasping sound. She dropped it on the dark counter and snatched off the cover.

She held up in her stiff, blue-veined, ringed fingers two limp little black hands sewn together at the wrists.

"Fifty-nine cents," the woman said in her sharp

old voice. Marcy put on the dark counter the piece of green paper she had been clutching. The woman snatched it up, dropped the little black hands and some coins into a bag and slid it across toward Marcy.

There was one thing more which had to be done.

"If . . . If-they're-not-all-right-can-I-bring-them-back?"

"Why shouldn't they be all right? It's what you asked for. Black silk gloves, size five. Why shouldn't they be all right?"

Marcy did not know. She reached for the bag and went to the door. She did not think she was going to be able to open it. She thought it had frozen shut. But when she put down the bag and used both hands it yielded.

She was outside, alone. There was nobody else anywhere, except the woman in the dark on the other side of the door.

But then there was Bess, and her father with both mittened hands high, pulling hard on the reins. Marcy climbed into the sleigh.

"You get warm in there?" He was trying to tuck the buffalo robe around her with one hand, his eyes on Bess's head. "The lady have the gloves?"

"She wasn't there."

"The store wasn't closed, this early?"

"No. Somebody was there." She dropped the bag on the seat between them.

"Give you any change?"

"It's in there."

They said nothing more until they were nearly home.

Then Marcy asked, "Will Aunt Vinnie marry Fon?"

"I don't know." After a minute he added, "I shouldn't wonder."

"Will Fon live with us?"

"I don't know," he said again. "That's their business."

She hoped Fon would live with them. She hoped he would be in the kitchen when they got there, with presents. She hoped her mother would be there, too, getting supper, and that after supper there would be pipe smoke and rolling words and everybody together listening and laughing. She hoped nobody would ever go away again, to Heaven or to Oregon or even to the village, but stay all together in the kitchen, snug and happy, hearing Fon's stories.

But Fon was not there, and Frankie was not there. Verd gave Vinnie a long white box and Vinnie showed Marcy what was in it. It was full of white flowers. Marcy did not like them. Vinnie put them in the cellar.

The next day they all went to the funeral. The sky was dark gray and spitting snow.

The yard at Clarence's was crowded with horses and sleighs. People went in the front door and sat on rows of chairs. The room was cold. The shades were drawn at the two front windows and the only light came in pale from the north. In the corner there was a big white velvet box on a table almost covered in white flowers. Nothing was familiar. Everything was strange.

Someone far off began to sing. Marcy knew who was singing. It was her mother's voice. At first it trembled. Then it grew strong.

Shall we gather at the river
Where bright angel feet have trod —

A man in a long black coat read from the Bible and talked.

Marcy heard him say:

"Earth to earth ... Earth to earth, ashes to ashes ... Earth to earth, ashes to ashes, dusk to dusk ..."

Dusk to dusk ... *Dusk to dusk.*

Frankie was singing again. It was the voice which had sung to Marcy many times, but with a strange tone in it, a tone which did not take Marcy in. It went away and left her.

We shall meet beyond the river,
By and by, by and by —

Dusk to dusk. By and by. Beyond the dusky river, by and by.

A different man in a long black coat appeared in the doorway. Beyond him the outside door was open to the gray sky, and gray snow, and the dark bare branches of the trees creaking in the wind. It was very cold.

He called names in a low, sad voice, and men and women walked two by two past the white velvet box and the white flowers, out of the dim room into the gray world. Dusk to dusk.

"Harold and Marcia Hasty."

Hal, who was sitting beside Marcy, stood up, took Marcy's hand, and drew her up beside him. He began walking toward the white, but Marcy's feet would not move. She looked around for help, but there was no one to help her. The few people left in the room were strange men — or looked like strangers to Marcy — and women with bowed heads covered in thick dark veils. The room was filled with soft sobbing.

"Come, Marcy," Hal whispered urgently, pulling on her hand. *"Come!"*

But she broke away from him, burst out in monstrous howls, and ran howling through the doors and through the yard where all the silent people stood in the bitter wind. Howling, she found her grandfather's pung, climbed into it, and hid under the robes.

It was a long time before they found her, and when they did she would not speak to them. She sat silent and stiff between Vinnie and Hal all the way home. Frankie did not come home that night. She could not leave Lula and their mother.

The house was dark but warm. Vinnie lit the lamp and fixed supper. Marcy had thought she would not eat, but there was easy talk at the table. George and Verd spoke of cousins they had seen that day for the first time in years. Vinnie said she remembered visiting them in York when she was a little girl and they had an express wagon they could steer downhill like a sled. Marcy slipped into her chair and ate beef stew with dumplings.

A little while after supper Vinnie said, "I guess we're all tuckered out. We'd better go to bed early. Why don't you sleep with me tonight, Marcy?"

Lying together in the dark, they talked. George could hear them talking, through the thin wall which separated his room from Vinnie's, and Verd could hear them in his chamber overhead.

"Auntie."

"What?"

"I know what the man meant, earth to earth. Kind
of. I know they were going to put the white velvet box
in the ground, and the baby Ruth was in it. But what
did he mean, ashes to ashes? Were they going to burn
it?"

"No. That wasn't what he meant at all. And the
baby wasn't in the velvet box. God took the baby three
days ago to live with Him. There was nothing in the
box but the clothes the baby isn't here to use any more.
So it doesn't matter to you what the minister meant.
It's hard to explain. And it doesn't matter."

"Yes, it does. Especially, dusk to dusk. Dusk is almost dark. Did he mean for everybody? Everybody
just goes from almost dark to almost dark? After dusk
it's black night."

"*Dusk?* . . . Well, Marcy, we can't see very well in
the dusk. When we remember as far back as we can,
it's dusky before that, isn't it? And when we try to see
God and Heaven with our own eyes, from here, that's
dusky too. So we do all go from dusk to dusk, but that's
all right, because we live our day between; and I don't
believe there is any black night at the end. Out of the
last dusk the heavenly sun rises and never sets. The
minister said that, but you weren't listening or you
didn't understand. '. . . in sure and certain hope of the
Resurrection unto eternal life.' "

After a while Marcy asked, "When is Fon coming
again?"

"Fon? I don't think he will come again, at least

for a long time. He has gone back to Oregon."

"I wish he wouldn't. I wish he would come and stay. I like Fon."

"You do?"

"Yes, you do, too, don't you?"

"Yes, of course."

"You're going to marry him, aren't you?"

"No."

"Why not?"

"Because . . . to like a man is not enough reason to marry him. Love is more than liking. And in a good marriage there is more than love. There is respect. And confidence."

"Don't you — respect Fon?"

"Not enough. Not as I respect the men in my own family. At his age they all knew what responsibility was and were carrying it. We had two grandfathers long ago who were soldiers in the Revolutionary War, and one of them had two sons fighting with him. My own grandfather was a Union soldier and so were his two sons. Your grandfather had cleared this land of trees and stones and built this house and barn before he was twenty-five years old. If I ever marry, it will be to a man who does more than roam around in search of adventures he can tell tall tales about."

George sighed in relief, turned over, and went to sleep. He always knew Vinnie had a good head on her shoulders. She could never be swept away as his other daughter, Hattie, had been at sixteen by a man with a little black mustache who danced with her at a Fourth of July picnic on the mountain.

"If you like Fon, why don't you play with the doll he gave you?"

"I thought," Marcy answered slowly, "it was like the baby. Like the baby Ruth."

"That's silly. It isn't at all. It's brand-new. Like the baby your Aunt Lula is going to have soon, a lovely, well baby that she can take into the woods with her when she goes blueberrying, and Uncle Clarence can toss up in the air, and your grandmother can feed her good bread and butter to. Only this one is yours, and you ought to play with it. You ought to name it, too."

A little later Marcy asked, "When is Mama coming home?"

"Tomorrow, she said. She said to tell you so. I thought I had."

Upstairs, Verd put out his hand in the dark to the empty space beside him, and knew she would come tomorrow. Early tomorrow. He would go up for her before he went to the shop, before Vinnie and Hal went to school. She would be here through the day with Marcy, and through the night with him.

"I'll play with — her. Tomorrow," Marcy promised drowsily. "We'll think — of a name — for her. Mama and I . . ."

MARCH

MARCH is the daybreak hour of the year. The face of the earth is still dark but the shadow is lifting. A pattern, seemingly aimless, is now discernible upon it, great patches of slate-gray snow, brown grass, and blue-green spruce and pine coarsely sewn together like a linsey-woolsey coverlet. The sky is a shade lighter; the red star is fading and sets early, while Leo the lion, his glowing heart a badge of courage pinned to his chest, romps across the southern sky in endless pursuit of the elusive Beehive. The winds, which all winter moaned and whistled, strengthen, attacking bare branches, chimney, and eaves with a hungry roar.

In the air itself we feel, smell, taste, see a change as delicate and tentative as it is undeniable and certain. Though hurled against us by the wind, its touch is as soft as the wing tips of angels. Its ethereal warmth, too slight for registry on the thermometer, seeps through our heavy clothing. Its fragrance has no name, being not from anything that is, but from all that is to come.

Its flavor is as wine to the veins. It spills a pearly sheen over the hills, the outcropping ledges, the fence posts, even over every brown blade, blue-black needle, pool in the ditch, and every pebble and grain of sand in the road.

To us, all of whose senses are as exquisitely responsive after the frozen months as the eyes of a man long blindfold and now unbound and led into the light, March brings a silent ecstasy, a still excitement, matched only by that of a woman suddenly pausing, hushed, incredulous, yet sure she feels the first faint, fluttering motion of a longed-for child.

The Gordian knot is loosed. The eaves begin to drip and the silver streams are blown by the roaring wind into a rainbow spray. The voice of the brook is heard in low gurgles and chuckles. The sap is rising.

The outer world reaches into the fastnesses of country life, unlocks doors, and even draws country people into it.

George Hasty was serving on the grand jury. Somewhere to the north, in bleak November, a farmhouse had burned to the ground in the night and the bones of the woman who had lived there had been found in the ashes. Her husband said he had been in Boston on business at the time, but no one understood nor could he satisfactorily explain what business he had in Boston, and it was known that he had insurance on his buildings and that his wife had money in the bank in her own name. The man had been apprehended and held all winter in the jail at the county seat. Now George was there, listening to the evidence for and against, with the duty to decide whether this man had set the fire with intent to murder his wife.

He had been away from home through the week for a fortnight now, riding behind Old Bell to Alfred each Sunday afternoon and returning on Saturday morning, but tight-lipped about what transpired in the courtroom, though we were all curious to hear. He said that he would tell us when the case was concluded. In the meantime, he spoke only of his nights at the boardinghouse and of the food there, which was good enough, all right, but the piecrust was a far cry from Vinnie's; thick and leathery with no gloss on top.

"Handles it too much," said Vinnie. "Best way is to cut the lard in with cold knives, and then roll it so thin you can almost see through it. A little milk dabbed on makes the gloss."

Vinnie is always free in telling how she cooks, but nobody else can do it as she does.

One Wednesday the temperature stood still at noon. By two o'clock it had dropped close to freezing. This happens now and then in March. It does not last, but it happens.

From behind her big desk at the schoolhouse, Vinnie told her pupils, "Any of you who have sap buckets out too far from the house for the womenfolk to bring them in may be dismissed now to empty them. The sap won't run much more until it warms up, and if it freezes may burst your buckets."

Hal was one of those dismissed, as of course Vinnie knew he would be. She was as interested in every cupful of his sap as he was. Nothing in the world better than fresh maple syrup on fritters for breakfast.

Hal ran most of the two miles home and when he got there the thermometer on the porch read twenty-eight. He shook his head in admiration of the way his Aunt Vinnie could tell how cold it was by the feeling of the air on her face, as she could tell the heat of the oven by opening the oven door and putting her hand inside.

"She let us out to get in the sap before it freezes," he shouted to his mother, through the kitchen window. "Marcy want to come with me?"

Frankie was sewing, as she always is on Wednesdays. She took pins from her mouth and answered, "Too cold and rough for her, out in this wind. But it's from the northwest. I'll rig her up and she can watch you from the porch."

Marcy watched him pull out from the shed the two sets of small, wide wheels which he called trucks, held together with one board, and put a tub on it. First he emptied the buckets hung on the pine spigots driven into the three big sugar maples her father had set out in the yard when he was younger than Hal now.

Frankie, glancing out, wondered why it did not occur to him that he should do this last, instead of hauling a gallon or two of sap all around the farm. Later she was glad he had done it when he did.

Marcy watched him set off across the field toward other trees he had tapped. As he was disappearing from sight down over the first hill he turned and waved to her. She thought she might still be able to see him from the top of a pile of new boards beside the barn, and went out and climbed it, using as a ladder the ends of the edgings

which separated the boards. She could not see him, but
Frankie saw her and called her back to the protection
of the porch.

Marcy stood for a while smelling the handful of sawdust she had scraped from the boards and held in her
mitten. Lifting it close to her nose, with her eyes closed,
she could imagine that she was in a room built of the new
boards, or in the hollowed-out heart of a great pine tree.
Then she began sifting a small stream of it to the porch
railing, making a tiny road, thinking that if she were
lost in the woods like Hansel and Gretel she would rather
have sawdust than crumbs to leave behind for her res-
cuers to follow. Birds would not pick up sawdust.

A crow called down angrily, "Caw! Caw! Caw!"
She looked up at him, black against the sky, and laughed.

The sawdust was all on the railing now, except what
clung to her mitten. She bared her other hand and stood
patiently picking off the separate grains. Every grain
was precious, if she was to be followed by it through
the woods and brought safely home.

"Mar — cy! . . . *Mar — cy!* . . . MAR — CY!"

She retraced her steps to reality by way of the crow,
thinking for a minute that he was calling her name.
She had heard that crows could be taught to talk.

But the crow was nowhere in sight, and the call was
coming from the southwest, from the row of trees which
separated the lower meadow and the pasture. She looked
steadily in that direction and discovered that what looked
like a strange branch moving out of unison with the
wind was an arm in a dark sleeve.

"Can — you — see — me, Marcy?"

She jumped up and down and screamed, "I see you, Hal! I see you! . . . Mama, Hal's 'way up in the top of a tree!"

"Funny place to be gathering sap," Frankie answered.

"What you up there for, Hal?"

Marcy could not tell whether he heard her words, but he knew she was answering.

"I'm — seeing — the — world! I — can — see — China — I think!"

"You can't either see China. Auntie says China is *under* the world. If we dug a tunnel right straight down through to the other side — "

"Marcy, don't yell like that," Frankie told her. "I should think it would split your throat. I know it's splitting my ears."

"Tub's — full," Hal shouted from the treetop. "Coming — home — now — to — empt' — it. Six — buckets — all — full — left — on — the — trees. Have — to — come — back." Marcy saw him start down. He vanished behind the hill, as if someone had waved a wand.

Marcy stood waving an imaginary wand until her mother came to the window and said, "Down to twenty-five. You come in now."

She was still slowly unbuttoning her long black leggings by the stove when Hal came in with a handkerchief bunched against his face. The handkerchief was a wet red ball.

"Nosebleed?" asked his mother. "Sit down and tip your head back. I'll get you a clean rag — "

He sat down and she quickly made a pad of a square of sheeting from the top bureau drawer.

"Not my nose, though," he said, giving her the handkerchief. "I got a cut. Slipped coming down that tree and caught on the stump of a broken limb."

"That'll teach you that climbing trees gathers no sap," said Frankie cheerfully. "As I told Marcy — "

But when she looked at his cheek she said, "Good gracious sakes alive, that's more than a cut. It's a jagged, three-cornered tear, and it's deep. I believe I can see your jawbone. Does it ache awfully?"

"Didn't, until I came in where it's warm. Bleeding's kind of stopping now, I guess. Soon as it does, I've got to go back for the rest of that sap."

"I don't know. I wish Vinnie would come. Or we had a horse here. I don't like the looks of that. Dark flakes in it, like bark pressed right into the flesh. I think the doctor ought to clean that up."

"Oh, you can clean it up, can't you? No worse than splinters."

"Yes, it is, too." Frankie stood looking at it for a minute, touched his cheek, which was beginning to swell and harden in an angry ridge around the wound, and came to a decision. "No, never mind the sap. You'd better start right now for the village. Probably meet your father on the way, and he'll turn around and take you to the doctor's. So you'll be back here by dark. He'll give you the money to pay the doctor. Now you get started. Somebody may come along to give you a ride."

They both knew it was not a likely time of day for getting a ride into the village, but they knew too that once he met his father it would not take fleet-footed Bess long to carry him into town and back.

He set off grumbling. "That sap freezes, bust the buckets."

"*Burst*," Marcy called after him smugly. She stood at the window, watching him grow smaller and smaller, singing, "Bust the buckets, burst the buckets, bust the buckets, burst the buckets," thinking, "When it's buckets, *bust* sounds better, but you have to say *burst* even when it sounds worst." *Burst, worst.* That was a rhyme. Was it poetry? She would ask Auntie as soon as she came home.

"If you're going to sing," sighed Frankie, "*try* to put a tune to it."

She skimmed a pan of milk and started a boiled custard. That would be something Hal could eat. His face was bound to be stiff. She set the cream aside to whip. Hal craved cream, and while his grandfather was away on jury duty was a good time to have it. George was always thinking of the butter a cupful of cream would make to sell to his customers. She would flavor the cream with nutmeg and a dash of vanilla.

"Does he know where the doctor lives?" asked Marcy.

She was remembering the village as she had seen it one day in the winter. A high brick wall which seemed to have no end and no beginning, with many doors; but all the doors were closed. Behind which door would the doctor be?

"Everybody knows Dr. Ross's house," her mother answered.

Then he did not live in the village, thought Marcy. He lived in a house.

Vinnie came, and when she heard that Hal had left

his sap in the shed, she went down with a dipper and pails and brought it up and turned it into the big copper kettle on the back of the stove. Then she brought in water from the well, and had Marcy help her bring up the night's wood. This was Hal's work, which he could not do because he had gone to the doctor.

"You have to say *burst* even when it sounds worst," said Marcy. "Is that poetry, Auntie?"

"No. It's just a rhyme. And not a very good rhyme. Worst of what?"

"Worse than *bust*. When it's buckets."

"That's worse, if you think so. Not worst. But poetry is first of all in the thought or the feeling. That has to be beautiful. And then the words you use to express it have to be beautiful as well as beautifully put together. Poetry is beautiful thought distilled. Boiled down like sap to make syrup."

"I don't see why they don't come," said Frankie. "It's almost dark. And supper's ready."

"Set it back," said Vinnie, taking off her hood and hanging it on a peg in the entry. "Likely enough the doctor was on a call and they had to wait. If he's out in the country, frost going out of the ground as it is, no knowing when he would get back."

Marcy stood staring, as if Vinnie had spoken in a strange language. She could not keep up with Vinnie's mind which darted so swiftly and easily from pie to poetry, from the seven wonders of the world to firewood, from hemlines to boundaries, from Scripture to sap. Where Marcy's attention was caught it stayed . . . *Beautiful thought distilled . . .*

"Maybe I ought to have tried to clean him up here, and bandaged it. Let him wait until his father got home. But he said it didn't ache so outdoors."

"What's done is done," said Vinnie. "We can't change it. From what you say, it was a job for the doctor. Walking won't hurt him. We might as well eat our supper now. Your tea always braces you up. Then we'll work on that coat you're making."

"What if he started to bleed on the way? Oh, dear Lord, I'd never forgive myself!"

"He would expect you to," said Vinnie. "For He would forgive you. You used your best judgment. That's all anyone can do. Nobody has any reason or right to have guilt feelings over an honest mistake. When we've made one, it's our duty to learn from it. That's one of the surest ways to learn. If you'd kept Hal here, he might have been too late in getting to the doctor. Now here's your tea. How far have you got to on the coat?"

It was seven o'clock and Frankie was running up sleeves on the machine, Vinnie leaning close to the lamp making buttonholes, and Marcy writing on the blackboard when Bess pranced into the yard.

Hal came into the house while his father went on to the barn to unharness.

"What you got to eat?" he mumbled. "Starved. Both starved."

His cheek was covered from his neck to his cap in a mass of white. He looked as if he had only a little more than half a face. But he had two eyes.

Frankie remembered that her grandfather — Grandpa Brooks — had said, looking for the first time into the cradle where his first-born great-grandchild lay, "What a handsome pair of eyes! Them eyes will make their mark in this world."

Hal had been almost all eyes then, and for years afterward. Often Frankie and Verd had thought they would lose him. Frankie's mother had come several times to be with her at the end. Keeping vigil at night, she would tiptoe over, shading the lamp with her hand, and look down to see if he still lived. Once he had opened his eyes and said with age-old weariness and infinite patience, "Tet down, Grammy. Tet down and read your Bibly book." Another day, when they thought he was going, his Uncle Clarence stood at the foot of the crib, tears on his hard, brown cheeks, wishing he could pull out with his strong hands some of his own woodsman's sturdy health and vigor and give it to this frail little boy he loved as his own child. He stood there a long time, and suddenly Hal opened his eyes and smiled and said in a weak chirp, "Sink I do, Conchie," because "Think I do" was a favorite expression of Clarence's and "Conchie" was Hal's name for him.

You cannot give your own strength to the weak, but you can help them to find their own.

"Well, you look as if you had just come from the battlefield," said Vinnie, glancing up from her buttonhole. "A Union victory, I hope?"

"Been took prisoner," Hal replied with half a grin, "and not even fed watered-down pea soup. But I got away."

"Not *took, taken,*" Marcy sang loudly at the black-

board. "Not *bust, burst.* Not *took, taken.* Not *bust,
burst.*"

"The sap I didn't get must be froze over by now,"
said Hal. "But not thick yet. Maybe I ought to take a
lantern — "

"Not *froze, frozen,*" sang Marcy at the top of her
voice. "Not *bust, burst.* Not *took, taken.* Not *froze,
frozen — "*

"Marcy, stop that noise this minute or you'll go
straight to bed," cried Frankie.

"*Tak-en, froz-en,*" said Hal mincingly. "Maybe I
should have tak-en a lantern in case the sap is froz-en
and the buckets should burst-en."

"Marcy, come over here," said Vinnie. "I'll cut you
a buttonhole to make."

"You're not going out of this house again tonight,"
Frankie told Hal, seeing him all eyes in the cradle, limp
and white in the crib, weighing no more at the age of
four than a healthy two-year-old. "I'm making you
some milk toast. That won't need any chewing. And
I've boiled a custard. You can have whipped cream on
it. What took you so long?"

Hal had kicked off his boots and sat now with his feet
on the leaf of the open grate, spreading his toes to the
warmth.

"Well, took me 'most an hour to get to the village.
Muddy most of the way, and down through Old Swamps
the bottom had dropped right out in places."

"Father said it would, you know," Vinnie reminded
them. "He told the road commissioner last summer the

foundation he was putting in down there would never hold in mudtime. The answer he got was, 'Well, now, George, if it don't, they'll have to elect you commissioner next Town Meeting.' And like enough they will. He's been elected to just about all the other jobs nobody else could do . . . Thread over the needle, Marcy. Every time, thread over the needle . . . That's it.''

''You had to walk all the way?'' asked Frankie. ''Your father hadn't even started?''

''No. He wasn't even at the paint shop. He'd gone to deliver a meat cart and was waiting for his pay. I didn't know where he was, but I had a piece of arithmetic paper in my pocket, and a pencil, so I wrote that I was going to the doctor's and pushed the paper under the door, in case he came back. And he did.''

''So he went down there for you.''

''Yep. By then I was in the doctor's office, but his wife told Papa I was there and he waited. The doctor took quite a while. First he burned it out.''

''Burned it!''

''With acid, he said. Then he put a lot of stuff on it. It foamed. Just like soapsuds.''

''Peroxide,'' said Frankie. ''I thought afterwards I ought to have put that on before you left. I've got most of a bottleful in the cellarway cupboard.''

''Then he sewed it up and bandaged it.''

''Sewed it!''

''Took seven stitches.''

''Will it leave a scar, I wonder?'' Hal's dear face scarred!

"Sure. I guess so. He said prob'ly would. What do I care? Who wants to be a pretty girl: *tak-en, froz-en.*"

On the way to the table where his mother had put his steaming bowl, Hal joggled Marcy's elbow.

"You stop that," she shrieked. "You made me prick my thumb."

"A prick!" scoffed Hal. "Now ain't that terrible?"

"And stop saying *ain't!*"

"Don't bother Marcy," said Vinnie. "She's making quite a nice buttonhole. And we'll have no more grammar lessons tonight."

Verd came in for the milk pails.

"Can't you eat first, Verd? You must be starved almost to death."

He said no, the cows were more uncomfortable than he was, three hours past their milking time. Frankie made him a sandwich of a big biscuit with crisp salt pork, to stay his stomach.

"Hal's worrying for fear the sap he didn't get may freeze hard enough to burst the buckets."

"Wind's moving into the south. It's warming up. Sap won't freeze any more. May melt. He can go down first thing in the morning and empt' them."

"That's March for you."

Hal was eating at the end of the table, Vinnie in her chair at one side, and Marcy in her grandfather's place. Frankie sat down across from Vinnie to wait until Hal was ready for his pudding. They had him between them.

"Hard for you to swallow, is it?"

"Nope. Goes down slick."

"I should think you'd be too worn out to eat."

"He'd better not be worn out yet," said Vinnie. "Too young to wear out."

"Too young to go through so much, seems to me. I kept thinking after I sent him off — all that way alone, and goodness knows how much blood he'd lost. Remember, Vinnie, he won't be fourteen till next month. What if Verd hadn't gone back to the shop and found his note? Would you have started to walk home, Hal?"

"What else?"

"You wouldn't have got here before nine o'clock. And there's no moon tonight. I'd have been half out of my mind. But of course your father would have gone back to meet you — "

"Hal's great-uncle Columbia, my mother's little brother, was only fifteen when he was set upon by ruffians on a dark night near the stable where he worked in the village. Set upon and drugged and enlisted under another man's name in the Union army," said Vinnie quietly. "Grandmother Brown didn't know for weeks and weeks what had become of him. But then she got a letter in his own hand. He said a very strange thing had happened to him the night he left, but he did not tell them what it was. He said he was in the army and that his comrades told him he would be sent home if he told what had happened to him and how old he was. But he said now he was there he would see it through; said he had been through two skirmishes without a scratch. He told her to write to 'John Maddock,' as that was the name he was enlisted under."

"What was his real name?" Marcy asked.

"Brown, of course," Hal told her. "Columbia Brown."

"Mother always called him Little Columby," Vinnie said. "He was only seventeen when he died. You can read the dates on the gravestone in the corner of the field. But he was more a man at seventeen than some are at seventy."

Uncle Columbia had been a Union soldier at fifteen. A year from now Hal would be almost fifteen.

"They say young men make the best soldiers," Hal said. He added, "You have to be young to fight. And tough."

Marcy stared at him.

"Will Hal be a soldier?" she asked her mother.

Frankie shivered and said, "Of course not. The country is free and united. We won't have any more wars." She brought the pudding.

"You never can tell ahead," said Vinnie. "It's best to be ready."

Verd came in and washed and took his place beside Frankie. She brought his supper of corned beef and potatoes and cabbage. He grinned at Hal.

"I see they have you on soft stuff."

"I'll be chewing tomorrow," Hal boasted.

"I had to eat that kind for six months once. Didn't stick to my ribs much."

"Before you were born, Hal," Frankie said, "the second year we were married, the doctor said he had appendicitis. Said there was nothing to do but be careful what he ate, and if the pain got bad enough he would operate but your father might not live through it. It came summer and he couldn't work, so I got a job help-

ing in Goodwin's candy store at the beach; we made all
the candy, Mrs. Goodwin and I, and Mr. Goodwin sold
it at the counter. I thought being out in the sun and
the salt air might give your father strength. But one
night he got such dreadful pains Mrs. Goodwin said why
didn't I put a mustard plaster on him. I didn't know
as I ought to, but I had to do something. So I made a big
one and put it on and he eased off and went to sleep.''

''When I woke up, I had a blister a foot square,''
laughed Verd. ''But I felt fine, and I went downstairs
and ate my fill of what I'd been smelling and longing
for ever since we went through the door of that candy
store — bananas and peanuts! And as Uncle Columby
Warren used to say, 'They feyed on my stomach neat.' I
never had that pain again, from that day to this, and
within a week I was painting signs for stores at the
beach.''

This was the only sickness Marcy had ever heard of
which she thought she might like to have. One to be
cured by peanuts and bananas. She would not, she was
sure, have kept on any plaster which would make a
blister. She studied her thumb in search of the place
where the needle had pricked her.

''Times like that, when a doctor has done all he can,
people have to do for themselves as best they know,''
said Vinnie. ''Folks used to do everything they could
think of, in time of sickness, *before* they called the
doctor. I don't doubt my mother or yours, Frankie,
would have put a piece of pork on Hal's cut, and let it
go at that. They used to think flesh to flesh was the best
healing, and a good many times it worked.''

"But if your father had had a doctor set that broken bone in his leg, he wouldn't have had eczema in it all these years. That eczema is the poison coming out."

"He didn't think it was broken, he always says. He was two miles deep in the woods when he fell, and he walked home on it."

"I don't see how he could. You can't walk on a broken leg."

"Well, he did. And you can tell it was broken by the way it's bent."

"Why, anybody else —"

"Well, Father isn't anybody else. Little Columby wasn't anybody else, fighting his skirmishes at fifteen in a blue uniform. Hal isn't anybody else, hustling four miles through the mud to get his face stitched up. Come, it's bedtime. Frankie, you'd better see to Marcy. She's half asleep here. I'll pick up the dishes."

Marcy, passing Hal dreamily, suddenly leaned against him. Sometimes she liked to lean against people.

"I guess you could be a soldier," she said. "I guess you're brave. I'd be afraid of walking in the dark. I'd be afraid of going to the doctor's. I couldn't find where the doctor lives. I'd even be afraid to climb a tree. If it was a tall tree."

"Of course you would," Hal answered, hugging her. "That's all right. You're just a little old girl."

"You wait," said Frankie, drawing Marcy with her toward the stairs. "Marcy'll be brave some day. In good time. Girls learn to be brave, too. They have to. How did I dare put that plaster on your father? How did I dare, when you were little, to give you medicine

so strong the doctor said it would either take down the
fever or — stop your heart from beating?''

"Well," Hal grinned, "it's still beating. Like a
clock.''

When he was alone with his father and Vinnie, he
stood up and yawned and stretched. Like Uncle Columby doing a man's job, like his grandfather after
walking home on a broken leg, like his father with a foot-
square blister, he felt fine.

He stopped at the end of the stove and looked into
the small mirror which hung above the comb case, seeing
his half a face and the white mass of the dressing.

The smell of sap simmering in the copper kettle floated
through the kitchen.

"Yes, sir," Hal said contentedly. "Yes, sirree. The
doctor says I'll have me a scar here that'll go wherever
I go, from now on.''

APRIL

APRIL is the two-week-old kitten, the month-old lamb, the six-month-old heifer, the two-year-old girl. Too young to know it has either past or future, it wears the ribbon of the fleeting present as part of itself — a crisp bowknot of iridescent taffeta changing with the colors of the sky from the pale pink of dawn to the pale blue of noon and the dusty rose of sunset. It dances on legs too unsteady to support it, but they are unaffected by the pull of gravity and touch the feathery pillow of the earth only to spring away. It never comes down where it went up. It vanishes, all legs, into a rainbow mist, and reappears all eyes; wide, wondering, tender, shining eyes which grow smaller and smaller, brighter and brighter, until they are like a shower of sparks, and like a shower of sparks go out. But long after that you can hear them singing in the soft, sweet dark with the voices of peepers.

Early that month the river overflowed its banks and water covered the railings of White's Marsh bridge. It was falling by morning but still too deep over the road for anyone to travel to town; Verd and his father loaded the dumpcart with stakes and barbed wire and went mending fences which must be secure for pasturing time.

After dinner that day Frankie was taken strangely ill before she and Marcy had finished the dishes. She pressed her wet hands to her head and lay on the couch, and her face turned white and she began to shiver as if with cold. Marcy dragged comforters from her grandfather's bed to cover her mother, but by then the whole couch was shaking. The comforters kept slipping off and Frankie's eyes were closed and her teeth chattered so, when she tried to speak, that Marcy could not understand what she said.

Marcy thought her mother was dying, and ran to call her father. She pulled on a jacket as she went but she had not stopped to put on rubbers, and as she ran down the pasture lane she felt water seeping in between the thick soles and cloth uppers of her buttoned boots, but it did not matter. If she had come to the brook she would have waded it. If she had come to the river she would have plunged in. But she came to pine trees growing so close together that she could see only the dozen aimless, winding paths cows' hoofs had made. She ran down one path and back and down another, calling, "Papa! Papa! Papa! Come home quick! Mama's awful sick!" She was lost, and stumbled to her knees.

"Papa! *Papa!* PAPA!"

He came, put her on his shoulder, and strode home. She smelled the pitch which spotted his blue frock, felt the warmth of his arms around her and of his neck

against her cheek, sobbed and said silently over and over
the words of the prayer she knew best.

*Dear God, bless Mama, bless Papa, bless Auntie and
Grandpa and Hal, and help me to be a good girl. For
Jesus' sake, amen. Dear God, bless Mama . . .*

The shaking had stopped. Frankie's cheeks were pink
and her eyes were open, glowing like the blue-black coal
from the mines of Pennsylvania which Fon Drew had
given her and which she kept on the kitchen shelf. Verd
built a fire in the little stove in their bedroom and carried
her upstairs and helped her undress. He heated water
and made her a cup of Jamaica ginger. The smell of it
was stout and cheering through the house. When she
began to shake again he held the covers over her with
his body and held her face in his big warm hands, pressing his fingers against her throbbing temples.

"It is a chill," he told Marcy.

When it was over, Frankie smiled at them both, and
asked Marcy for a glass of water. Marcy dipped it from
the pail; well water, best in the world, her grandfather
always said.

A little later Vinnie and Hal came from school, and
George drove the dumpcart up to the barn. Verd said the
river must be down enough so that he could get through,
and he would go for the doctor, now that Vinnie was
here to sit with Frankie, and Hal could help his grandfather with the milking.

All the pieces were falling into place.

Verd was back in half an hour, unhitched Bess from
the red gig, hitched Old Bell into the democrat wagon,
and drove back across the flooded bridge for the

doctor, who was waiting there in his automobile.

Dr. Ross is a short, thickset man with curly dark hair. He learned to be a doctor by working with another doctor and began by driving the other doctor's horse. He brought Hal into the world. He does not smile much, but his voice is low and gentle.

When he went into Frankie's room, Vinnie was there, for when a doctor is attending a woman patient another woman must always be with her.

Frankie was saying, "I've been lying here thinking about the Easter services we used to go to in Rochester when we lived up there. The whole chancel banked with great white lilies. Seems as if I can see them. Seems as if I can smell them. We ought to be where we could go to church. Why can't we go back, now Vinnie isn't going to get married? I miss my bay window and the street light that shone into it at night. I'm so thirsty. When Jesus asked for water, they pressed a sponge wet in vinegar to his mouth."

"She's burning up with fever, Doctor," Vinnie said quietly.

He nodded. He had left his hat on the newel post. Now he set his worn, round leather valise on the bureau and rubbed his hands above the little stove.

"Fold back her sleeve from her wrist." He took a small case from his inside coat pocket and drew out a thermometer. "Put this in her mouth and tell her to keep her lips closed." He swung a chair to the bedside and bent forward, taking the narrow wrist between his fingers. "Well, Frankie, looks like you're down with the grippe, like a good many all over town." And a few

minutes later, "Hand me the valise. I'll listen to her
chest. Unbutton her nightgown. Nice, bright chamber
you've got here, Frankie. Always like a bedroom facing
east."

When Dr. Ross came downstairs, Marcy was setting
the table for supper and Verd was putting a pan of
biscuits into the oven.

"You chief cook and bottle-washer, Verd?"

"Well, I can mix up a batch of biscuits and drop
them out. I learned that in logging camps. Don't roll
and cut them the way women do. How did you find
her, Doctor?"

"Oh, she's got this grippe that's going around. It's
hit her hard because she's run-down from the winter.
Blood's poor. Tell that by her color. I've given her a
dose to take the fever down and put her to sleep. Lungs
are clear, so far. She'll be all right if we can keep it
out of her lungs. Frankie's lungs have always been
delicate. Let me have a couple of glasses half full of
water." He opened the valise and poured a thick pink
liquid into one glass, thin brown into the other. "Give
her three spoonfuls of this when she wakes up, and
every four hours after that or as near it as she's awake.
One spoonful of this three times a day." He shook out
big yellow tablets on the red tablecloth. "Get a saucer
for these, Marcy. See your mother takes one night and
morning. Build up her blood. Keep her on liquids for
the next couple of days, Verd. Soup and porridge, like
that. Ought to drink a lot. I told Vinnie I've got to get
up into Tatnic as soon as the water goes down; probably
tomorrow afternoon, after office hours; I'll call in here

on my way. I look for her to be easier by then. But she'll be weak. These things take a lot out of anybody, this time of year, and Frankie's not strong. Figure on keeping her in bed for about a week."

When Frankie fell asleep, Vinnie came down to the kitchen to strain the milk and finish getting supper, and Hal went up to sit with his mother and tend the fire in the little stove. Verd came back from taking the doctor to his automobile and they all had supper. Marcy took her plate and Hal's upstairs and they ate together, sitting on the top stair with the door of their mother's room ajar. They talked a little in whispers until Frankie called in her own natural voice:

"Who's that telling secrets outside my door?"

They hurried in and Hal turned up her lamp and Verd came up, two steps at a time, bringing the yellow glass and a spoon. She looked at it and made a wry face and they all laughed.

George called from the foot of the stairs, "Vinnie says does Frank want a good cup of tea?"

Frankie herself answered.

"Yes, Father. That's just what I want. Plenty of milk in it, tell her. No sugar. I want to get this sweetish taste out of my mouth. Marcy, you bring it. Save Auntie what steps you can."

"Why," Marcy scolded herself happily, "did you ever think Mama would die? Didn't you know we wouldn't let her die?"

She did not think Frankie needed the horrid medicine. She thought it was the fire in the little stove and Verd's arms and Vinnie's tea and Marcy and Hal whispering at the top of the stairs and George's voice from the foot which would make her mother well.

Will Dorr, who lives across the river, had seen Verd go down the road in the red gig and come back, and go again with the democrat wagon and return with the doctor. He spoke of it at supper. His wife, Grace, is Frankie's cousin and when these two were little girls they lived in the same house, for their mothers were sisters and one lived upstairs and the other down.

"Now who can be sick enough over there to have the doctor?" Grace exclaimed. "Vinnie kept school to-day, I know. Was Hal there, boys?"

Her Leslie and Clyde nodded.

"They say anything about anybody at home being sick?"

"No. Didn't say anything."

"Then it must have come on sudden. Or else it's Marcy or Frankie. Unless it's George, and I don't believe for a minute it's him because if he was on his deathbed he wouldn't call a doctor and none of 'em would dare call one for him, not even Vinnie. You don't suppose Marcy's picked up the scarlet fever they're having up Tatnic way? I don't see how she could, never goes anywhere. I hope to the Lord it's not Frankie. I haven't laid eyes on her since Lula's baby's funeral, but she's always peaked before winter's out . . . Will, if Verd could get over White's Marsh bridge, we ought to be able to get over ours. Soon as Bernice is abed and asleep, I want you to hitch up and take me over there."

Will said, "Guess I can get you across all right."

"If 'tis scarlet fever," said Will's mother in her deep,

slow way, "don't you bring it back into this house. You don't know what 'tis to have three young ones down with it. I do."

"If it's scarlet fever, I won't go in, of course. Neither will Vinnie and Hal go out tomorrow morning. There'll be no school and Frankie will have plenty of help; and so will Will and Father and Verd and George with their fencing. But I can't rest tonight until I've at least been to the door and found out."

Everyone else at Dorr's was asleep when Grace tiptoed down from the finished chamber and Will folded his newspaper and went to the barn to harness. Grace tidied her soft, ruddy-brown hair, put in her best side combs, turned the lamp low, threw a shawl over her shoulders, and ran out to climb into the wagon beside Will. The dark was warm and foggy, and the only light they had was from the lantern Will gave to Grace to hold. As they lurched through the ruts of the road which ran along the edge of the field, beside the woods, Grace suddenly laughed aloud.

"What's funny?" Will asked.

"Not funny. Nice. Exciting. Almost like eloping. When did you and I ever ride out alone by night before?"

"Quite a night we picked for it," he said as the horse waded into the water which covered their narrow bridge.

But the horse was steady and Grace clung to Will with one hand, to the lantern with the other. They were soon over the bridge, into the black pool between the old willow trees, and up the rise to the main road. From there it was not far to the end of the lane and the Hasty house, where lamps still burned, upstairs and down.

"Lit up like a ship at sea," Will said.

"Oh, I do hope it's nothing bad!"

An iron weight on the end of a long strap would keep the horse where they left him. Vinnie had seen them coming and opened the door as they climbed the porch steps.

"Well, Grace!" she said low. "And Will! What are you doing out this time of night?"

"Will saw Verd bring the doctor, Vinnie. Who's sick?"

"Frankie. But no need to worry. It's grippe and she's run down. She had two or three chills. But she's asleep now. Come in."

"We don't want to wake her."

"You won't wake anybody. Come in."

They woke no one who was asleep, but Verd heard them from where he sat by Frankie, and left her door and Hal's ajar and came down the front stairs. Marcy heard them from her cot in the alcove and came down the back stairs. Her mother would have sent her back to bed, but her father and Vinnie didn't; they let her curl up on the couch with her bare feet tucked under her nightgown.

They talked low because George's bedrom was close by. Verd and Will talked of the flood, and of other floods they remembered. Vinnie told Grace just how Frankie was, and that the doctor said she would have to stay in bed a week; it looked as if Verd would have to be house-keeper for a few days; it was lucky it was Wednesday because Vinnie would be here to take over on Saturday.

Grace said that if the water wasn't over her boots she would come the next two afternoons while Bernice had her nap, so Verd could have a couple of hours a day to straighten things out at his paint shop if he wanted to and if Frankie was so that he was willing to leave her. Grace had brought half of a marble cake from her cellar cupboard, thinking Frankie would like it because it was by a recipe their mothers had used. Vinnie made cocoa and they all had a small piece of Grace's cake and some of Vinnie's filled cookies.

Marcy thought, "I never s'posed this afternoon we'd be having a party tonight." The creamy marble cake stuck to her fingers and she licked them sleepily.

When Grace and Will left, the cool, damp smell of the April night drifted into the chocolate-sweet kitchen from the open door.

"Fog's gone," Grace whispered on the porch. "Stars out."

"First thing we know," Vinnie whispered back, "we'll hear the peepers."

The next afternoon when the doctor came, Grace opened the door to him.

"Mercy's sake, Doctor!" she exclaimed. "*What* have you brought?"

It was an Easter lily.

"Patients keep sending them in," he said gruffly. "More than we've got room for. Eases their conscience, I guess, when they rout me out of bed of nights. Put two or three of them in the car today to leave along the way. Thought Frankie might like one. How is she?"

It did not surprise him that Grace was here. He knew

of the relationship, had brought all Grace's children into the world, too, including some she had lost, and knew that often it had been Frankie's hands to which he passed a new Dorr baby.

"I think you'll find her better. She's not very hot, and she's longing for an orange. Verd's gone to the village to get her some. I gave her a bath and combed and braided her hair. Oh, Doctor, that's the handsomest lily-plant ever I saw in my life!"

Marcy stood staring at it. Out of a big brown pot, long, tapering green leaves like the blades of swords, and out of them a thick green stalk with two great wax-white lilies fully bloomed, one bud half-open, and three tight-folded buds. What a strange thing to be on the kitchen table! She was not at all sure she liked it, but she knew her mother would.

Frankie liked it. She all but worshiped it. When Hal came home he brought in the night stand from his room and put it in front of the window nearest his mother's bed. Vinnie sent up a white, fringed cloth to cover it, and they placed the plant there. Frankie lay on her side, her cheek on her hand, and smiled at it.

"Marcy, take my Bible and put it beside the plant . . . Across the corner . . . That's it . . . It's like a little pulpit . . . I feel strength coming from it to me."

When Verd brought her orange, peeled and broken into sections, she asked for more pillows to raise her head and so she half sat, with Vinnie's little pink crocheted shawl around her, sucking the golden juice from orange sections and gazing at the lilies wax-white against the pale pink of the eastern sky at sunset time.

The lilies were in her room every day as long as she stayed there, and at bedtime were brought out into the hall. The strange fragrance was all through the house.

The next day when Grace came she brought white and green crepe paper, and with thread and Marcy's crayons she and Marcy tried to make lilies like those growing in the pot.

"Tomorrow maybe I can try it," Frankie said. "I wonder what would happen if we dipped them in wax. We could try one. I've kept a bagful of wax from my jelly jars, all clean and put away. We could melt a few. Verd must have some wire out in the barn we could use for stems."

It seemed to Marcy they were all the same age.

Grace and Frankie talked of the wooden dolls they had played with, and of the time they had walked hand in hand up the road to have supper with Little Grammum and spend the night with Grammy and Grandpa Brooks.

"Little Grammum was our great-grandmother, dear," Grace told Marcy. She called both Frankie and Marcy "dear" whenever she spoke to them. "Grandpa Brooks's mother. She was only three feet and a half tall, but they said Great-Grandsir — he died before we were born — was over six feet and so were all their sons. Remember, dear," to Frankie, "at home they all thought we would be back before dark?"

But when their mothers came up at bedtime to see how they were faring, Little Grammum said they had behaved like ladies, taking fish hash and johnnycake and cambric tea in her part of the house. ("We always called it the Hamilton house because Bial Hamilton built it around Revolutionary War time.'') And Grammy Brooks told Em and Louise that their little girls had sat on the door rock and sung hymns with them until it was time for Grandpa to take down his big Bible from the shelf and read a chapter and pray; and now they were sound asleep in the step-bedroom off the kitchen.

"Remember, dear, how Grammy had to boost us into that high bed? After she went out, we heard Grandpa feel around the bottom of the clock for the key, and wind it. Almost seems I can hear him now. Can't you, dear?''

"Yes. And the brook. I slept in that room many a night after that, and the brook sang me to sleep. So peaceful . . .''

"And that time we had the picnic up in Grandpa's pasture. That wasn't long before we were married, you know, dear. But Lula and Cathie and Maude were still small, and anyway we were all always like children with Grammy and Grandpa. Even Marm and Aunt Louise and Uncle Than. Remember we all played blindman's buff that day? Grammy tied Grandpa's handkerchief over our eyes and Grandpa spun us round — and how we all laughed!''

But Grace had current news to tell, too. Did they know? Had they heard? Will was off that day to buy him a pair of horses. Yes, sir, a matched pair! He and his father would widen the haycart and widen the woodsleds, and think how much more they could haul! What a saving it would be not to have to hire the plowing done!

And did they know? Had they heard? Men were

about to start setting telephone poles up this way from the village, and by summer the lines would be strung. Seven places along the main road had signed up for it already, and Emerys' — where Grace's mother lived, and Grace's sister Cathie and her family, and their brother George and his family — was one of them.

"One of the reasons Will's getting the pair," Grace cried, "is so he and Father and the boys can drag out trees. Then they'll peel them and set our own poles across the field from the main road, so by the time the line gets this far we'll be ready, and we'll have a telephone too! Why, dear, just imagine a box on the wall that I can go to and ring and speak to Marm any time I want to. Won't it sound like magic?"

Like magic, surely. Marcy trembled with eagerness to ask whether the box would carry Grace to Aunt Em's house or bring Aunt Em to Grace's house. Or would the lines be hung with rugs on which they could fly to meet each other? Without moving her head, Frankie turned her eyes for an instant to the Easter lily and the Bible with a silent prayer that she be helped, in her weakened condition, not to break the tenth commandment. What she would give to be able to hear her mother's voice today, or Aunt Em's for that matter! Or to have been able to go the wall and ask the doctor for advice when Hal hurt his face! Dorrs had and did so many things Hastys never had and did, or ever would. A pair of horses now! And when Dorrs had only one, Grace always had it to use at least one day a week; but here there was no horse for Frankie; only the men drove

Old Bell, and only Verd drove Bess. Dorrs all went to the Fair, one day or another, every fall; except Bernice, who was still too young. Charles Dorr never went to the village that he did not bring back candy for Bernice, a book or a feathered arrow for Leslie and Clyde, cloth for Olive to make into dresses for Bernice and shirts for the boys. Olive did all Grace's sewing, and often made as many as six new shirts or six new dresses in a week. George Hasty had never been known to buy a present, even as much as a piece of candy, for anyone; brought home only flour, sugar, saleratus, molasses, and often seemed to begrudge the use of that, as of eggs and butter and cream.

"Remind me, Lord," prayed Frankie, "that I have never lost a baby. And that Grace has other crosses to bear. She does not speak of them, as I don't speak of mine. But I know what they are."

"Why, Grace, you'll have a Brooks picnic every day," she said.

"Yes, and you must come over, dear, and call up anybody you want to that's got one of the telephones," Grace ran on, for she hasn't a selfish bone in her body. "It won't cost anything to use it. We have to pay so much a month whether it's used or not. I guess Marm will be surprised, first time she hears your voice over it. Suppose she'll know who 'tis? Oh, we'll have a real frolic . . . And Will says to tell Verd he'll plow for him free this spring — and George, too, if he wants him to."

"No reason he should do it free."

"Plenty of reason, dear. Verd could help him get used

to handling the horses. Besides, hasn't Verd cut Will's hair and the boys' free for years? Will says he does a better job than any barber he ever went to.''

''Oh, they started that when they were boys together.''

''Well, it's no different now, dear. And Will likes to do a favor as well as the next one.''

So toward the end of the month, on a Thursday which was Hal's fourteenth birthday, Will came with his matched pair to do the plowing, and Grace with him to help Frankie get the dinner, and Bernice to play with Marcy.

They came after an early breakfast, and the grass was still so wet that the mothers would not let Marcy and Bernice off the porch. Grace turned the washbench on its side, said, ''There, that's your house. Now you both be dear, good girls,'' and went into the kitchen where Frankie was churning because, plowing day or not, she always churned and made out the butter on Thursday.

The girls stared at each other as at strangers. Marcy is two years older than Bernice, but they look near the same age, for Marcy is short and stocky, Bernice tall and thin. Bernice has yellow braids and eyes the color of the April sky. Marcy's braids are brown and her eyes are hazel like her father's. Marcy's pomponed cap and scarf with fringed ends were brown. Bernice's pomponed cap and scarf with fringed ends were blue.

''You can be the mother,'' said Marcy at last.

''Can I? I like to be the mother best.''

''So do I. But I have to be the father because we don't have any baby yet and I'm the one who knows where the baby is so I can bring it to you. That's the only way a mother can get a baby. The father has to bring it to her.''

''I didn't know that.''

''It's so. I asked Mama and she told me.''

Marcy brought out the doll Fon Drew had given her, and the trunk now filled with clothes, and some broken dishes.

''Here,'' she said. ''You can dress the baby while I mix up a batch of biscuits and drop them out. I don't roll and cut them the way women do. You can dress the baby but don't carry her around. You might drop her. You just had the grippe and I had to get the doctor for you. First I had to carry you upstairs. I can carry the baby and I can carry you. I'm strong, and I *never* get sick. I was never sick but once and then I cured myself by eating peanuts and bananas. That was a long time ago. When we were first married.''

While they kept house on the porch, Grace cleaned the vegetables to serve with the corned beef Frankie had simmering, and Frankie made out the butter and stamped it into round, pale yellow cakes each weighing about a half a pound and with the design of a sheaf of wheat on top. Grace chopped and seasoned raw cabbage in a wooden bowl while Frankie made a custard pie in her favorite deep crockery plate, which is as big around as a milk pan. When this was in to bake, they sat down to look through sample catalogues, choosing the paper Frankie would send for to cover the walls upstairs. Until now the chambers and Marcy's alcove had never been papered.

''Oh — Marcy!'' Frankie called. ''The grass must be

dry. I put a cake of butter into a lard pail. You and Bernice take it up to Melissa Nowell. She loves fresh butter. Go through the field. It's almost time for the mailman and he may be driving an automobile. Your father's been painting one for him. I should think they could leave off their caps and scarves; shouldn't you, Grace?''

Bareheaded, braids bounding, lard pail swinging, unbuttoned coats flying out behind, Marcy and Bernice raced through the fields, up hill and down, to Nowells'. Old Melissa did not ask them in and they knew why, because they could see past her that she had just washed her floor. The wide pine boards, white from the scrubbing action of sea sand, were still wet in all the places Nowell feet had hollowed out.

"Hold on now while I git the butter out to give ye back the pail,'' said Old Melissa.

Her skirts were looped up halfway to her knees, showing her thin old shanks, and wisps of hair had escaped a quick pinning and hung over her ears. But every lamp in the long row on her kitchen shelf, placed in order of height, was filled and shining, and every chimney gleamed. There were seventeen lamps in the row. Marcy counted them.

"There. Here's your pail. There's sponge cakes in it for you young ones for doing of the errand. Tell your mother I'm much obliged. Careful now you don't upset the cat's dish on the step.''

They raced back and stood munching sponge cake; watched the men and horses come and go; watched the plow cleave the earth and turn it back open, damp and dark, for the seed, widening the great brown patch on the side of the greening hill; watched the pink angle-worms freeze for an instant as they first felt the air, then curl and disappear into the dark. They listened to the men's voices and the bird songs and the horses' feet and the squeak of the harness, and smelled the earth, the sweating horses, the hot sun on the new grass and new leaves, the wind blowing through the pasture pine and juniper.

They heard a strange, unaccustomed rumble. For the first time an automobile other than the doctor's came up the lane. The doctor's was black, but this one was dark blue with narrow red and gold striping. This was the conveyance of the United States Government. Men and children gazed at it and after it until it had passed beyond both sight and hearing, and the women's faces were at the kitchen window.

Marcy and Bernice raced to the mailbox, found not only a newspaper but a small package there, and ran with them to the house.

"It's Hal's present, Mama! From Widow Jones!"

"He always gets one on his birthday," Frankie told Grace. "He wonders every year if he will and he always has. Ever since Vinnie bought him some pants and a jacket for his sixth birthday when she was in Boston on a visit to Aunt Annie. He's supposed to get them from the company that sold the suit until he is twenty-one. Last year it was a ruler. A nice one, with a brass edge. Marcy, tell the menfolks dinner's ready."

There was an hour of splashing at the sink, eating and joking at the table, and sitting back to tell a few stories before Verd and Will went out to finish the plowing and George settled himself with tubs and baskets in the shed door to cut up potatoes for seed.

Marcy and Bernice carried the doll and broken dishes to the top of the boardpile by the barn.

While Grace washed the dishes, Frankie made a chocolate cake.

"I'll boil a frosting for it before supper," she said. "It's for Hal's birthday. He is a great one for chocolate cake. They're plowing one piece for Hal today, you know, and he's going to work it to earn money for clothes to wear when he starts in at the Academy next fall. I'm going to tell him that when summer comes, as long as he works well on his piece, I'll have chocolate cake on hand whenever he wants it with milk for a lunch. He says he could eat a whole one in a day. Well, we'll see. Of course they won't be frosted."

"Now, dear, why don't we write out the order for wallpaper? This with the red roses is going to be handsome up in your chamber . . ."

The order was just going into the envelope when Will hitched the horses to the barnyard fence and Verd went into the house.

"Good job done," George said from the shed door. "Quick, too. Glad to pay you, Will." Not that he would have been.

"No. That's all right. Verd says he'll drive for me next week if Father don't feel like handling the pair."

"You'll be home well ahead of milking."

"Not much, I guess. Verd's gone in to see if the

womenfolks want to get some mayflowers. They're bloom-
ing on the ridge.''

"Always bloom first up there.''

Verd came out carrying a pair of rubber boots in
each hand, and handed one pair to Will.

"The girls'll need these to get across the marsh,''
Verd said. "It's a case of carry the boots or carry
them. Grace didn't bring hers. She says she can wear
mine, but I calculate they'll be a mite big for her.''

"Will unless her feet's grown today.''

Frankie and Grace came out in their shawls, but the
sun was still hot and their heads were bare, Frankie's
blue-black like her eyes and the coal from Pennsylvania,
and Grace's ruddy and glinting gold in the sunshine.

"I'm coming with you, Mama,'' cried Bernice, looking
for the best way to climb down off the boardpile.

"Are we coming too, Mama?'' Marcy asked.

Their mothers looked at them as if they had forgotten
they had them.

"No,'' said George. "You young ones are better off
where you be.'' And to the others, "Go along. I'll keep
an eye on 'em till you get back or Vinnie comes. Take
me another hour or so to finish this lot.''

Marcy and Bernice watched their parents go without
a backward glance. As they crossed the lane and came
to the ditch Bernice and Marcy had jumped over, Verd
made a funny deep bow and offered his arm to Frankie.
Behind them Will did the same to Grace. Their laughing
voices came back across the field. Marcy saw that just
before they disappeared over the top of the first hill,

Verd slid his arm under Frankie's shawl and she knew that it was around her waist. She knew that in a minute Will's arm would be around Grace, too.

Bernice was crying a little. Marcy put her arm around her.

"Don't cry," she said. "When Margery-Madeleine is old enough, I'll take you mayflowering. But you know we can't go off and leave a baby."

"You young ones want another doll?" asked her grandfather. "Here's one for ye."

He had run wires into a big potato which was soft on one side, and put smaller potatoes on the ends of the wires for a head and hands and feet.

Marcy scrambled down for it and scrambled back.

"Anybody home?" she called loudly. "I'm back from the village with a doll for Margery-Madeleine!"

George Hasty never bought presents, but this was not the first potato doll he had made in his life. And he remembered other Aprils, when he and his Sarah Jane had gone mayflowering on the ridge.

M A Y

MAY is the tender promise we know will come true. If in the earlier months any of us has doubted that God loves His children, every one, we doubt no longer. The sun has come back and rises north of the mountain, gently flooding the windows of the east chamber as it comes up, and casting a soft light on the brown kitchen wall behind the supper table as it goes down. The grass is green and growing and the cattle are out. One night at milking time a new calf is brought up from the pasture. The seed is in and long rows of twin leaves rise from the earth. The apple trees are in rosy bloom, the blossoms of wild pear and cherry like white torches against the dark woods and the stone wall. Day and night the air is bright and sweet with the scent of budding fruit, the flash of wings, and the song of birds building nests among the flowers. The whistle of the first whippoorwill is a bugle call to summer.

But the hallmark of May in our countryside is the moss pink, called by many the graveyard pink because long ago a bit of it was set out in every family burial lot and flourished there as if it had a mission to spread a field of pink and white stars all over these hilltop squares, these upland corners, so that in May, at least, they could not be overlooked or forgotten. Whether or not these lots are fenced with granite posts and iron rods, whether they have white marble monuments or slate stones with names and dates or unshaped field stones with initials or no markers at all, all are marked in May by the moss pinks, and each family goes out to its own and sits awhile in the sun speaking of those who have gone. At other times, riding past the moss pinks, they speak of neighbors.

"There lays Shem's little Japhet," says George.

The moss pinks cover the solitary grave of a baby who did not live long enough to be given a name. But his father was Shem who had a brother Ham, and the Bible says there were Shem, Ham, and Japhet.

The Hasty cemetery has a fence of granite and iron and a monument bearing the single name of Sarah Jane Hasty, wife of George. To Marcy this seems a lonely place. She goes there only with Vinnie, who sets out plants in the urns and waters them.

"Why do you do that?" Marcy asked once. "You say Grammy isn't here."

"I do it to honor my mother's name," Vinnie answered. "This is where her name is. And always will be."

But Marcy does not like the urns, nor the fence and railings. She always wanders off in search of ivory pips or checkerberries or flowers. In May she goes to the edge of the moss pink field which has spread down the hill

toward the pines, and picks some to take home and put
in a cup beside her grandfather's plate at the table.
Since the first time he has not been surprised to see them
there. He may feel, as she does, that Sarah Jane sent
them to him.

The Warren cemetery down the lane from the Hasty
house, in the corner of the field where the lane joins the
main road, is one of Marcy's favorite places. The War-
rens were Sarah Jane's mother's family, and the stones
there bear her mother's and father's names; and that of
her brother Columbia who was born in 1848 and died in
1865. It has no fence, only the stones and a few trees —
a cherry tree, a maple, scattered small pines — a tangled
mass of Scotch rose bushes, and the moss pinks. They
have covered the whole corner, spread out into the field
to where bluets, violets, and Indian tobacco also bloom
in May, and run down over the high, sandy bank in
which Marcy digs with iron spoons in summer and makes
pies in cracked saucers with water brought in a lard pail.

She was there last Decoration Day morning when
the Civil War veterans came.

She had known they were coming. Until this year
she had supposed that the bright-colored flags, which
in May always replaced the faded and tattered rags on
John and Columbia Brown's graves, bloomed as the moss
pinks did. But the day before when Vinnie had taken a
pink geranium in a brown pot to Lydia Warren Brown's
grave, Marcy had asked: "Why didn't you bring geraniums for John and Columbia, too?"

"Men will bring geraniums for them tomorrow. With
the new flags."

"What men?"

"Probably Uncle Gran, and other men who were Union soldiers like Uncle Columby and Grandfather Brown in the Civil War."

"Will they have guns?"

"No. Just flags and flowers. The war has been over a long time. Since 1865."

"That was the year Columbia Warren died."

"Yes. He did not live to get home. He had started home, but he died on the way . . . Mother always called him Little Columby."

"Why did he want to go to war?"

"He didn't. But he wanted to make men free and to save the Union."

"Wasn't he free?"

"He had grown up free. Like you. But down South there were men and women who did not know what freedom was, for they had never had it. Other men owned them. They were bought and sold. That is slavery. And slavery is wrong. But many who owned them did not want to let them go free. When a law was going to be made that they must, their states seceded from the Union. So men who loved the Union went to war to bring them back."

The next morning early, Marcy hurried to the Warren cemetery. She ran off as soon as she had finished breakfast, and the dew was still on the grass. She did not know how long she would have to wait for the soldiers, and she wandered about making a little nosegay of moss pinks, bluets, and violets. The grass was too wet for her to sit or kneel, but the sun was warm and the short, tender stems of the flowers kept slipping through her fingers.

A bobolink flew out of a ditch and she ran to see where he had flown from. She put her flowers into her looped skirt, bent to part the grass, and saw the nest with four tiny speckled eggs in it. Two bobolinks swooped above her head and made angry sounds.

"Don't worry," she told them. "I won't touch your eggs. I know little birds are going to come out of them."

She backed away and the mother bird settled into the grass. The father bird circled watchfully above.

"You needn't be afraid," she told him. "You're free. You can fly wherever you want to and take any food you find. Your little birds will be free too. Next fall you can all fly south and in the spring you can fly back. How would you like it if people caught you and sold you?"

Then she heard wagon wheels creaking through the sand ruts. A democrat wagon, drawn by a white horse, had three men in it, two on the front seat and one on the back. She crouched behind a bush and watched through its curly new leaves.

Gran Hasty, Bill Hooper, and Elijah Boston are men in their sixties. Gran has white hair, but his face is smooth, pink, young around his white mustache, between his white hair and the white shirt he always wears, even when driving his cows to pasture. Gran and Elijah are big men, and Elijah's sandy hair is sprinkled with gray; but Bill is small and still dark, with a boyish look.

Marcy knew that Gran was Uncle Gran, her grandfather's brother, and that he lived in the house where he and her grandfather and their seven brothers and sisters had been born, the children of Joseph and Joanna Hasty; she knew that Joseph's grandfather and two of his uncles had been soldiers in the first war, the Revolution. She knew that Elijah Boston lived farther over the lane than she did, for she had seen him ride and walk past. She had seen Bill Hooper only in church, and heard his voice in the hymns above the other men's; all the Hoopers are singers.

She watched the three men jump out of the wagon without touching the iron step, which is for women and children. While Gran hitched his horse, Elijah climbed the bank carrying two small bright flags, and Bill ran up after him with a potted red geranium under each wiry arm. By the time Gran reached them, they had pulled up a few bushes of lamb's poison, and Elijah had the ragged flags in one hand. The new flags were flying, and Bill was on his knees, placing the plants close to the white stones. Gran stood behind them, checking off names in a small brown book. All three had taken off their hats and dropped them on the grass.

"John Brown was putty old to go soldiering, wa'n't he?"

"One of the oldest. But Sarah Jane always said her father was bound to go. He was one of the first from around here, too. Only lasted out there a year, and never was a well man after they sent him home . . . Soon as he got back, Joe went. And then Columby. All the boys John and Liddy had . . . I see somebody's set a plant here for Liddy. Probably Vinnie."

"Awful strange thing how Columby come to go."

"No stranger'n how he come back."

"Somebody musta been hard up for courage, to have a fifteen-year-old boy grabbed and sent out south under his name. Maddox, was it? Or Maddock?"

"The few letters he sent home, sometimes he spelt it one way and sometimes the other. Likely didn't know how to spell it. 'Twas a Concord regiment he was in, you know . . . He writ he could have come home if he'd told what happened to him that night he was took from his bedroom by the livery stable where he worked. But he 'lected to see it through, sence he was there."

"Give the devil his due, likely the one he wore the name of didn't know who went in his place. I used to hear if one was called up that didn't want to go, he'd pay so much — say five hundred dollars — to a gang to send one in his place, and knew nothing about who they got, or where, or how, long as one went and he didn't have to."

"Five hundred or a thousand, sold themselves cheap . . . And some way they didn't dare let Columby get home. You know he writ his mother he was in Concord, safe and well, waiting for his discharge. Next they knew, folks told 'em of a coffin marked 'John Maddock' on the station platform in North Berwick."

"Hard times, them was, for that family."

"Hard times for a good many, one way and another. Maybe harder for them at home here than 'twas for us. Still . . ."

"Them old cannons roaring and bullets zinging —"

"What you saw on a battlefield was worse'n anything that happened to you —"

"Marching and tenting was worse'n fighting. Colder. Folks here couldn't hardly believe how cold it can get below Washington —"

"Them swamp fevers so many died of. Like Ephraim Dow, Verd's wife's father. He lived to get home and get married, but he never shook off that fever, and died when she was only six months old."

"Ones like Ezry Goodwin, her uncle . . . wounded bad three times in three different battles. Gettysburg and Cold Harbor, and I forget what the other one was —"

"Maybe the prisons was the worst —"

"But a lot of us come through it all some way. We kept the Union together, and got a chance to start over again. A lot of 'em thought we couldn't do it, but I allus thought we could."

"They had some awful smart officers."

"I've heard 'em say the South had the brains and the North had the brawn. Guess we got stout from slaving for ourselves."

"Brains don't make right. Brawn don't neither. Slavery wa'n't right and splitting up wa'n't right. So we had to fight, and we was bound to win."

"We was on Old Abe's side, and he was on the Lord's, if ever a man was. You can't lose with generals like that."

"It took a long time, though. Four years."

"Yep. Generals can't fight a war. It needs young fellers, like we was, to keep at marching and pitching camp and marching agin and shooting it out until it's over. So I don't believe even the generals know how long it's going to take, when it starts."

"How could you tell?" asked Marcy, standing up, strewing all the flowers she had held in her skirt.

They turned and looked at her.

"Tell what, little widgit?" Gran asked.

"Which side God was on in the war."

"That's putting it to ye," Elijah chuckled. "Answer her that, Gran." He told Bill, "Verd's young one."

"Mind, I didn't say God was on anybody's side," Gran told Marcy slowly. "I said Old Abe was on His, and so we was on Old Abe's. I figure that's what counts, studying till it hurts — the way Old Abe did — to find out what, to the best of your belief, God wants done. Old Abe studied and prayed hard, and he figured God didn't want this great country tore apart, and neither did He want black men and women owned by white men; and the only way to prevent both was to fight. Either that or give in to slavery or give in to have the country divided. So we fit."

"Why didn't God make it so you didn't have to? Why didn't *He* let the slave people go free?"

"Out of the mouths of babes," said Elijah, admiringly.

Gran shook his head.

"God made us and put us on this world. What we do here is for us to choose. If He was to do everything for us, what use would we be? Some people got it into their heads to make slaves of other people, and it was up to people to get it out. Way we figured, that was a job God give us to do, if we would. And we've allus been putty proud we done it for Him, little widgit . . . Your grandpa to home?"

[93]

"No. He's gone to market."

Gran laughed.

"Might have known. It's Friday. If the Judgment comes on a Friday, Gabriel will have to let his horn cool till George gets back with his butter and egg money . . . Well, Bill, we better be getting along with the rest of our load, if we're going to finish time for dinner and get back to the village for the formation. You coming up along with us, Lige, or is this the parting of our ways till afternoon?"

"I better strike off over the lane from here," Elijah said. "It's some'at of a walk. But what say we give 'em a song first? You start us off, Bill."

He threw his arms across the shoulders of the other two. Bill and Gran had put on their hats, but they took them off now and held them in both hands, over their stomachs. Elijah's hat still lay on the grass at his feet.

A stiff breeze blew out the two flags. The red geraniums stood tall. The moss pinks reached out to the bluets and violets and Indian tobacco. The sun shone down bright and hot on the American earth, on the graves of the old soldier and the young one and of the woman who had watched them go and waited for them to come back, on the three men in like blue trousers held up by suspenders, and on the little girl whose heart was beating so hard she thought the men must hear it like a drum.

Bill Hooper turned his small, dark face toward the sky and began in a clear tenor:

Yes, we'll rally round the flag, boys . . .

Gran came in with the air and Elijah with the bass.

> *... we'll rally once again,*
> *Shouting the battle cry of freedom!*
> *We will rally from the hillside, we'll rally from*
>   *the plain,*
> *Shouting the battle cry of freedom!*
> *The Union forever, hurrah, boys, hurrah!*
> *Down with the traitor and up with the stars!*
> *While we rally round the flag, boys, rally once*
>   *again,*
> *Shouting the battle cry of freedom.*

The three voices died away along the sandy roads, across the quiet fields, and up the course of the brook toward its source in the side of the mountain. In the hush which followed, the men put on their hats without speaking. Elijah climbed down the bank and started over the lane; Gran and Bill got into the front seat of the wagon, which still had a few flags and a few plants in the back, and rode away.

The ground was warm and dry now, and Marcy lay down on it, full length beside Columbia's grave, among the moss pinks, but leaning on her elbows with her chin in her hands.

She thought about dying. The baby Ruth had died in the winter and the boy Columbia had died about this time of the year in 1865. Many other soldiers had died that year and in the earlier war years. Her Grandfather Dow had died not long afterward of sickness from the southern swamps when his child, Frankie, was only six months old; Frankie had a tiny pair of red leather shoes with straps and green glass buttons which he had made for her first Christmas.

When the baby Ruth died, Vinnie had told Marcy that only her clothes were buried in the ground. Marcy understood now that Vinnie had meant a body is like a shirt or a dress a person wears, part of the clothes he needs on earth, but doesn't need when he goes to God, and leaves it behind . . . So young Columbia's body was here beside Marcy, and his father's and his mother's, but *they* had gone away long ago.

"From dusk to dusk," she had heard the minister say at the baby Ruth's funeral.

"We all do go from dusk to dusk," Vinnie had agreed. "But that's all right because we live our day between, and I don't believe there is any black night at the end. Out of the last dusk the heavenly sun rises and never sets . . ."

If God was to do everything for us, what use would we be? What we do here is for us to choose . . . Way we figured, God give us a job to do, if we would. And we've allus been putty proud we done it for Him . . .

The dates on Columbia's stone were not far apart. His day between had been a short one. But in it he had set people free.

Marcy spread her hands and looked at them. They were square and pink-palmed like her father's and her Aunt Vinnie's; not long and slender like her mother's and Hal's.

"They're mine," she thought. "To do with."

She sat up, and took a fold of her skirt between each

thumb and forefinger, looking at it; then a fold of the flesh over each pink knee . . . her clothes. She was still in them, because she still needed them. What was it that she needed them for?

She stood up, and the world stretched away on all sides of her. The moss pinks covered the quiet graves, mingled with the bluets and the violets and the grass, and the grass spread over hill and dale to the silent woods which were on all sides. The road and the lane were clean white ribbons across the green, the river a dark one flowing silently, without effort or intent, toward wherever the ocean was. Behind all, toward the east, was the mountain. Over all was the still blue sky. This God had made. This, and Marcy.

As far as eye could see in any direction, she was the only one anywhere. Marcy, with a blue butterfly swaying on a cherry blossom, and the brown head and shoe-button eyes of a bobolink half hidden on a nest.

Marcy felt small for the first time in her life.

She thought, "I'm so little."

Then she stood on tiptoe, spread her arms, took a deep breath, smiled, and thought, "But — I'm important. I'm the only one here. And this is my — day between."

As if the thought were a signal to life, sound, action, and reaction, a screen door slammed in the distance, and a familiar caroling cry came from a little to the west of north.

"Coo-oo-hoo-oo-hoo-oo!"

Marcy turned toward the sound, saw Bernice jumping up and down on the Dorr well-curb, and gave a responsive hop.

"Coo-oo-hoo-oo," she answered.

Lately they often made contact in this way and so, as they played alone, played together.

But this time Bernice was not playing. Still calling, she ran down the hill from the pump, crossed the little bridge over the brook, and ran up the hill on the other side. There she stopped, and called again, pointed ahead, and ran on toward the river which flowed between them.

Marcy understood that Bernice was bringing a message to the riverbank, and ran across the main road and through the Old Joy field to receive it. Soon only the swirling dark water separated the two small figures.

"Mama says," panted Bernice, "do you and your mother want to go with us to the parade? Papa was going, but he and Grandpa think they'd better plow a piece on the point today. So there's just us going. And there's room —"

"What parade?" Marcy asked, amazed. "Where?"

"The Decoration Day parade. Down to the village. The soldiers march. We went last year. I had an ice cream cone."

The soldiers marched. That was what Uncle Gran had meant by getting back to the village "for the formation."

"Oh, I'll see," cried Marcy.

"Mama says we ought to leave in an hour. If you can go, come out and coo-hoo. I'll wait by the pump."

Five minutes later, Marcy was at the corner of the Hasty house, jumping up and down and coo-hooing. An hour later Grace and Bernice rode out of their field

into the main road, and Frankie and Marcy were waiting
for them in wide shade hats, and dresses that fluttered
in the wind. Leslie and Clyde had come ahead on their
bicycles to open the gate, and Hal was there on his to
help close it. As the horse trotted down the road with
his train of ladies, the boys flew past them, pedaling furi-
ously, wheeled and came back, and passed them again.
They made quite a parade of their own, and the farther
they went, the more top buggies, open buggies, democrat
wagons, carryalls, and bicycles were ahead and behind
them, filling the sandy road. Some of the horses had
red, white, and blue rosettes at their ears, and many of
the bicycles had small flags on the handlebars. People
who were not on the way to the big parade stood in
their fields, yards, or doorways and waved at this one.

One man, at his planting, threw his straw hat into the
furrow, stamped on it, and sang:

> *Tramp, tramp, tramp, the boys are marching!*
> *Cheer up, comrades, here they come —*

Frankie said, "Wes must have something stronger
than ginger water and molasses in his field jug today."

Grace laughed.

"Oh, Wes is always full of the old Nick, dear."

When they had crossed the bridge and the railroad
tracks of the Eastern Division of the Boston and Maine,
the station agent with a green shade over his eyes waved
from the depot window. They could hear the telegraph
ticking behind him.

They went on through Old Swamps, past the big

village cemetery which was like a big garden in which flags bloomed among the flowers, and came to Verd's paint shop. He was standing in his doorway, and surprised to see Frankie and Marcy in the Dorr wagon. Grace turned in there, and he hitched the horse for her, and walked down to the Soldiers' Monument with them, smoking a cigar. Marcy stared, for she had never before seen a cigar. She thought it smelled delicious, and that it made her mother proud to walk beside him while he talked and puffed, and pointed with the hand that held the cigar between thumb and forefinger. In the crowd by the Monument she looked hard at all the faces and figures, comparing them carefully with Verd and Frankie, and had no doubt that no other father was so well built as hers, stood so straight, had such an open, handsome, friendly face, wore his hat so jauntily, held his cigar with such careless grace; no other mother was so slender, dressed so like a queen in filmy blue, had purple eyes, or wore so wide a hat of lacy brown straw which showed her dark hair through the lace and had a pink silk rose all floppy on the side and let the sun make a soft, mysterious pattern of light and shadow on her lovely face.

Marcy thought, "I must be a princess. Nobody says so. They're keeping it a secret. But I must be."

She looked about anxiously for Prince Hal. He should not get too far away. Somebody might kidnap him and leave another boy in his place . . . But he was only across the street with Leslie and Clyde. They had been to the stores and bought flags which they were fastening to their handlebars.

Now from the west came the sound of drums. People stopped talking and faced toward the sound. They saw a white horse coming up the middle of the street as if he were dancing slowly. Behind him three men carried three flags as big as a man can carry in a pocket on his belt. As the horse and flags came into view of the massed crowd by the Soldiers' Monument, the thin, sweet music of the fifes joined the beating of the drums, and the sun flashed on the instruments. Behind the Fife and Drum Corps marched the soldiers of the Grand Army of the Republic, more than twenty of them, four abreast, in their blue uniforms and visored caps with G.A.R. in brass letters on the front. Some of them had white hair and some of them were lame, but they were in step and stared straight ahead. All their faces and hands were brown, their eyes were bright, and their faces were proud.

We've allus been putty proud we done it for Him . . .

Behind the marching soldiers came a great float, a truck covered, wheel spokes and all, in white crepe paper. White as snow, with tiers like a wedding cake. On the lower tiers, in red chairs, sat the soldiers who could not march — two who were blind, three who had lost a leg, several who had grown feeble — but all in their blue uniforms, and all with proud faces.

We've allus been putty proud . . .

On the top tier stood a beautiful lady in white, with a red, white, and blue sash, a gold crown, and what Marcy thought was a gold scepter.

"Papa," Marcy whispered, "is that a queen?"

"That's Liberty," Verd answered, low. "The Statue

of Liberty. That's the torch of liberty in her hand. It's what the soldiers fought for.''

Then Liberty made people free. Liberty was Freedom.

And at the white steering-wheel of the float were the strong dark hands of a man with the darkest face Marcy had ever seen.

''The man driving,'' she whispered, ''was he one of the — the slaves the soldiers freed?''

''John? No, John wasn't. But his father was. And his mother, too.''

''*Bought? And sold?*''

Verd nodded. Frankie glanced at Marcy and shook her head. Bernice was very quiet, holding her mother's hand. Marcy said nothing more.

But she watched the free dark man driving the float which carried the blind soldiers, the one-legged soldiers, the sick soldiers, and saw that his face was as proud as theirs.

''Because now,'' she thought, ''*he* is helping *them*. That's what makes people proudest. To do what God wants done for people who deserve it.''

Behind the float marched a hundred Sons of Veterans, and behind them hundreds of children carrying flags. All joined the crowd around the Monument, filling the green triangle and the streets on both sides. The band stopped playing. A great wreath of red and white flowers tied with blue ribbon was placed at the foot of the Monument. A minister prayed. A boy not much older than Hal stood where the minister had stood and spoke strange, wonderful words Marcy did not understand but never forgot:

"Fourscore and seven years ago our fathers brought forth on this continent a new nation, conceived in liberty, and dedicated to the proposition that all men are created equal . . ."

When he stopped speaking, the band began to play again and everybody sang:

Speed our Republic, O Father on high,
Lead us in pathways of justice and right;
Rulers as well as the ruled, one and all.
Girdle with virtue, the armor of might;
Hail! Three times hail to our country and flag!

That was all. That was the end. That was Decoration Day.

Those who had been singing together drew apart and walked away, or climbed into carriages and rode away, and most of the children, including Marcy and Bernice, had ice cream cones. The sun went down the sky, and all over the United States people were going home to supper.

JUNE

JUNE is the stirring call of youth to youth, and all that is young in the world responds with vibrant vitality. A rising chorus of bright new sounds, a glorious burst of fresh new colors, a heady mingling of rich new fragrances, and an effervescent rush of sparkling new emotions change the whole sweep of the landscape and work magic in the senses of all who walk upon it.

The hinge may still be as rusty as it was last winter, but no matter; its creak is not heard, for the door stands open and the room is filled with the shrill, sweet, full-throated songs of mated birds; the joints of the old, oiled by the dry warmth of the longest, sunniest days of the year, creak no more.

The great trunk of the shagbark hickory may curl and prickle with age, but its heart, its ardor, soars in its mighty branches, its strong leaves, its nuts young as the morning and invulnerable within their stubborn little olive burrs. And who sees a prickly or mossy old trunk, when a hundred dancing shades of green brush the sky,

a riot of blossoms ranging from the wax-white of syringas
and Scotch roses through the shell-pink of peonies and
hundred-leaf roses to the deep cerise of lilies and
ramblers cover the stone walls, rim cellar holes, and
bank or climb up the sides of low houses, when the spread
of field and pasture is lavishly embroidered with white
daisies, yellow buttercups and wild strawberries?

Not only house doors and windows, but cellar windows, the bulkhead, and the great barn doors are wide
open, day and night. As the winter dust and frost are
gone from the house, so are the stored meats and
vegetables used from the cellar and the barn lofts nearly
cleared of last year's hay, the stanchions empty except
at milking time. All the smells of winter are washed
away by the flood tide of the perfumes of June — an
incomparable blend of a thousand flowers caressed by
the sun, of fruit springing from the bud in the orchard,
of roots thickening in loose, rich soil, of sea turn, swamp
mist, running brooks, birch and pine. The outdoors comes
in and there is no indoors.

A new queen has ascended the throne. The queen is
young, strong, and beautiful. Her name is Nature. The
house is her footstool, the sky her royal cape, the barn her
stable awaiting her blue horses with arched necks and
flying white manes and tails. All people have become her
people, but not her slaves nor even her subjects. She
has come to set them free of whatever has enthralled
them, dubbed them all knights and ladies, and endowed
them with some of her own infinite capacity to delight
and to be delighted.

Small children, barefoot, roam at will, wading brooks,

peering into muskrat holes, feeding small birds in the hollows of trees, following woods trails, digging in sandbanks. Women's fingers are pink-stained at night from the picking and hulling which bring strawberry shortcake to the table. Men's faces and hands turn deep brown, in startling contrast to the white of the upper half of their foreheads revealed when they take off their broad-rimmed hats and of their forearms when they roll up their sleeves to wash at the sink for supper.

Swing chairs, fresh-painted, are set up in the yards, and in the warm, sweet dusk before bedtime two women or a man and a woman sway there face to face, suspended. If it is a man and a woman, they are in love, whether declared or not, and whatever their ages. If it is two women, they sing or dream of love, either past or hoped for. Garden chairs are brought out, and on Sunday hammocks are swung between chains which hang from tree branches. A girl or a woman lying in a hammock on a June Sunday afternoon is a lovely thing and knows it. If a man is there, he brings a garden chair and sits beside her. If he is her man, he may bend forward as he talks and take her hand; and she is fulfilled and content.

But those of school age only taste the season, cannot drain their full share of its nectar until Last Day.

This year Vinnie had her Last Day of school on a Saturday. Usually the exercises are held on Friday afternoon and the children and their mothers go to the Piece Speaking in the clothes they wear to church. But this year Vinnie said the exercises would be at eleven o'clock on Saturday morning, the girls might wear their favorite school dresses and the boys their usual overalls and shirts if they had clean ones. She said she had her reasons and would say no more except that of course they must all wear shoes.

"Shoes hurt," grumbled Henry, "after I ain't wore 'em for a month."

But Vinnie was adamant. Shoes must be worn for Last Day.

"*Jehoshophat!*" almost-swore Henry as the already toughened soles of his brown feet struck the pedals of his bicycle and whirled him out of the schoolyard. "Wish to *thunder* she'd have it Friday and get it over with."

From the school door Vinnie looked after him with special fondness. He is the only pupil she has ever had to discipline severely more than once.

She remembered those difficult times, and remembered many others when Henry had amused or touched her. Even the difficult times had been more so for her than for him, and she was glad of that now.

"Hold out your hand, Henry . . ."

Mischievous eyes twinkling almost on a level with hers. White teeth flashing in a wicked grin. Thin shoulders humped from hands clasped behind his back.

This was a moment he had been waiting for:

"Here I stand before Miss Blodgett,
She's going to strike — and I'm going to dodge it!"

She let him have his moment, and get his laugh from his audience. Then:

"Your hand, Henry . . ."

It came. He did not dodge. And he kept his grin.
Later she heard him tell the others, "There's a knack to
it. Bend your fingers way back. Makes your hand so
hard you can't feel nuthin."

Henry was the one who, when he was no more than
six, came into school at the call of the bell one morning
chewing. He was still chewing lustily when Vinnie
opened her Bible to read the daily lesson.

"Henry, go outside and dispose of whatever is in
your mouth."

He went, and they all waited for him to come back.
When he did not, she went to the door. He sat on the
top rail of the fence, still chewing.

"Henry, spit that out and come in and take your
seat."

He shook his head violently, tucked his quid into his
cheek like a chipmunk, and explained, "It's beefsteak.
My father bought and paid for it and I ain't going to
waste it."

Vinnie saw the logic of this, and that, as he must have
been chewing for a half an hour already, it was highly
uncertain when he would be finished.

She left him there and from behind her desk gravely
told the others, "We will have our morning devotions
without Henry today. He will be in later."

It was also Henry who a few years ago brought her
in a salt bag a little rosebush he had dug up from
beside an old cellar hole. It blooms now every June by
our back steps. Vinnie calls it "Henry's rose."

Friday afternoon was like any school day afternoon,

and Last Day was Saturday this year. Vinnie had her reasons.

All the parents knew one of her reasons, but kept it secret from the children, which was not easy. The little ones at home wondered why, after Friday's weekly cleaning, the women untied the dustcloths from their heads, sighed, set their lips, and began the baking which was Saturday work. The older ones, rushing in at four o'clock with, for the first time, only dinner buckets to drop — no books — sniffed and asked, ''We got company coming to supper?'' The answer they all received was short. ''No. I'm trying to get ahead of myself for once,'' or ''No. Now you skidaddle out of here.'' They were all glad enough to skidaddle into the fields or woods until chore time. Before they came back, the men had brought the ice and covered it over in a dark corner of the shed. The churning and packing was done after the young had gone to bed. Only the childless used swing chairs that balmy night.

Saturday morning the girls were surprised that their mothers did not don Sunday silk or muslin but only the afternoon percale or gingham. The boys were amazed to find that many fathers were going to this Last Day, wearing clean overalls like the boys' and white shirts open at the neck. When wagons were drawn up before the doors and loaded with what looked like tubs covered in black rubber blankets, and women brought out armfuls of boxes wrapped in newspaper to stow under the seats and then ran back for more, no one could doubt that this was more than an ordinary Last Day.

But those who asked questions were told gaily, for now everyone was in a holiday mood, "Never you mind. Go scrub behind your ears. Use a *cloth!*" or "Curiosity killed a cat. Your hair ribbon is untied."

What puzzled Hal and Marcy most was that Verd drove Old Bell out of the yard with only Frankie on the seat beside him and only them on the back seat of the democrat wagon. It was not to be expected that their grandfather would go. George Hasty had never been into the schoolhouse, except to deliver wood, since he left it at the great age of seventeen, having completed the study of world history, trigonometry, and surveying under the tutelage of his neighbor, Sylvester Chadbourne, whose brother Paul was the president of Williams College out in Massachusetts. But George still had the books in which he had studied, the cost of which, along with the cost of the flannel and serge for the shirts and pants he wore to school, he had earned by working six months of each year at the Portsmouth Navy Yard.

George was in the field, planting his second crop of peas.

But why was Vinnie still up in her room?

When Marcy had asked, Vinnie said, fastening her pink cambric collar with the pin in the shape of a new moon and a sparkling star hanging from it, "I'll come in a few minutes. You go along with your mother."

How would she come? Would she be there on time? No one else had the key to the door. Last Day could not begin without the Teacher.

The four rode slowly behind Old Bell down the lane, into the main road, and down Warren's hill where an

everlasting spring bubbled up through the red sand
of the ditch and flowed out across the stony hillside. The
water looked good. It was already a hot day. Verd
let Bell follow her own thought and turn to the right
just before they reached the bridge, wade into the brook,
and turn her head as if asking, "Well, are you going
to let me have some, or aren't you?" Hal walked out on
the shaft and unfastened the checkrein. Bell drank deep,
and they all waited, listening to her draw the cool water
into her long neck and swallow it gratefully. When she
lifted her head at last, Hal fastened the checkrein and
brushed a fly off her ear before he climbed back into
the seat beside Marcy.

From there on, the road was thickly wooded on both
sides for a way. The deep shade was welcome, but to
Marcy this section of the road was always an adventure.
She suspected the hidden presence of Indians, and was
sure there must be a wolf den near by, though she had
been told that the last wolf had disappeared toward
Canada when her great-grandmother was less than two
years old. Even when they had come out, quite suddenly,
to where the houses were so close together that the
flowers from the garden of one had spread into the yard
of another, she kept looking behind her, for she remembered the story of the wolf pack which had once followed
a horseback rider here on his way home from the grist-
mill. To gain on them in the life-or-death race he had
thrown off first a bag of grain, then a second and then
his third and last bag of grain, and finally his coat. Thus
he had ridden into his barn and closed the door just
ahead of the howling pack . . .

But now the bridle path has become a sunlit, sandy road with deep ruts through which narrow, steel-rimmed wheels roll silently unless they hit a small stone washed down from the hills. The horses' ironshod feet pad in sand between two rows of feathery grass. All the little houses, save America Warren's old black one clapboarded in virgin pine, are painted white, with green well-houses or red pumps, and all the barn doors stand wide open, unafraid, in June. All the houses are on the left of the road, to face south, and the river runs behind them, every spring flooding the points of land at its bends to produce the best of soil for both hay and pines.

Ahead Old Glory, full of a lively breeze, billowed from the top of the schoolhouse flagpole.

The Hastys passed Nason's Eddy, the square white church and the little white parsonage where no minister has lived for a long time, and followed the road away from the river, passed the old Emery house on the right, and rode up into the yard of The Red Schoolhouse at the fork of the roads. The first district schoolhouses in town were unpainted, the later ones painted white, and all these are called by their number; but this one is The Red Schoolhouse. It has a more generous yard than any of the others, and stands out against the big maples which border the roads on two sides of it and the woods on the south where the boys have cleared out the underbrush and made a playground with a big rope swing and two smaller ones.

Several teams were already hitched in the shade, but Verd found a place for Old Bell among them, and Verd and Hal joined Verd's old schoolmates and their sons leaning against the fence. Frankie moved into one of the groups of women and older girls standing self-consciously under the trees in their straw hats and skirts which caught on the grass and lay in blue and brown and sprigged black-and-white swirls around their hidden feet like the bases of figurines. Only the small children ran about and they did so aimlessly, coming close only to members of their own families, for here they did not feel that they knew even their nearest neighbors well.

The schoolhouse door was still closed. Last Day could not begin until it was open.

At six minutes of eleven by Jotham Warren's gold watch the Teacher, Vinnie, came.

She came in an automobile which was left down by the Emery pasture bars so that the horses tethered in the schoolhouse yard would not be startled. The horses had pricked up their ears at the sound but could not see the machine because of their blinders. Only the people and the pastured cows stood staring. This automobile was like a buggy without a top, had only one seat, and its wooden body was painted yellow.

"It's like my express wagon," thought Marcy. Her Uncle George and Aunt Hattie Webber had brought her one from Eliot for her birthday, which was not until next week. "Only bigger. And it runs up hill as well as down."

"One of the first ones," Verd told Will Dorr. "Like them I painted after they first begun coming into Rochester. Been kept up, though. Looks like new."

Its driver walked up the road behind Vinnie in her pink cambric dress with white hamburg lace and insertion at yoke and cuffs and around the full skirt, her little white lace hat with pink forget-me-nots under the rim, her filmy pink scarf which had protected her hat and hair while she rode and which now floated from a white-gloved hand.

Coming into the schoolyard she smiled at the children, nodded and spoke to the women, calling some of them by their first names, and with no self-consciousness at all approached the men by the fence.

"This is Mr. Bannister, Verd," she said. And to the man behind her, "My brother will make you acquainted, Mr. Bannister. I have a few matters to attend to inside before eleven."

She disappeared into the schoolhouse, keys jingling, closed the door behind her, and began opening windows at each of which her face and raised arms flashed and vanished.

"Who is *that?*" whispered the women near Frankie.

"Mark Bannister," Frankie answered low with a faint smile. "Has a big farm down below Webbers' on the Depot Road toward Kittery. She met him last spring when she was visiting Hattie. He's been writing to her but this is the first time he's been up here. I've never seen him before."

"Don't look like a farmer."

Mark Bannister was a tall, thickset, middle-aged man with heavy dark hair and deep-set eyes. He wore matching pants and coat of fine dark wool, a white shirt with a blue tie, a straw hat shaped like a felt one, and a gray cord vest with a gold chain looped from pocket to button-hole and to another pocket. One of the pockets must hold a gold watch, of course, at least as big as Jotham's, and the other, the women guessed, a penknife with a mother-of-pearl handle. He also wore a ruby ring.

"No," said Frankie. "Well, I hear he hires men to do the work on his place. He's somebody high up at the Navy Yard. George Webber was speaking of it when he and Hattie were up for dinner last Sunday. Vinnie hasn't said anything about him. Except this morning she told me he was coming today, and she would ride up with him. He hadn't come when we left."

"Ain't married?"

"Was. Wife died a year or two ago, Hattie says."

The women hummed, comparing Mark Bannister with their husbands who leaned against the fence, some of them smoking cob pipes and two chewing tobacco.

"I *wisht* he wouldn't," thought one; and "Mine's full as handsome when he's dressed up," thought another.

"Guess she didn't tell *him* to wear his overalls," said one.

"Makes the rest of 'em look 's if they'd just come from the barn."

"Maybe he don't own a pair of overalls."

"Oh, of course he must," said Frankie. "George says he has a lot of stock and makes pets of his animals. Can't go around animals in a store-bought suit . . . Our men-folks don't notice the difference, probably. They're comfortable."

The men were talking louder now, telling stories of fast horses and balky cars, big snakes, big fish, and weasels in henhouses. Mark Bannister listened, turning from one to another, shaking his head in admiration, and sometimes laughing. He had a deep, rumbling laugh.

It is men who find common ground, women who are set apart by differences in mode of conveyance, apparel, and manner of speaking.

"I don't suppose it's her place to tell him what to wear, is it, dear?" Grace asked Frankie. She added, "Yet."

"I should doubt it." Frankie smiled. "As I say, she's never mentioned him to me. Until this morning."

"She's pretty well fixed up herself, though," said another. "Can't be she's worried about grass stain as she warned us."

"Vinnie's always fixed up," Grace reminded them.

She always is. When she came to the door without her hat, gloves, and scarf, she looked as much like the other women as she ever does, or a teacher should. She looked as usual for a school day in June. She looked as her pupils were accustomed to see her.

She rang the bell, and said, "Take your places, children."

They fell into line and passed, as always, in a column as she stood beside the step. Where a space between was too wide, she narrowed it with pressure of a hand on a small shoulder. One little girl dropped a thimble she had, for some purpose known only to herself, been wearing on her finger. Vinnie, unsurprised, picked it up and tucked it into the child's pocket.

When the tallest had passed her, she said "Please come in" to the guests, and followed him.

The women moved slowly to the door, taking the

hands of their small children, glancing curiously at the men who moved still more slowly, even reluctantly, after knocking out their pipes against the fence.

The first woman to reach the schoolroom gasped.

"Why, it's like fairyland, dear," Grace whispered to Vinnie behind her hand, as if they were in church.

Vinnie and Hal had worked there late, by lantern light, the night before.

The teacher's desk had been moved to the back of the room, and behind it a crisp new flag covered the blackboards. Red, white, and blue strands of crepe paper were looped to the tops of the four walls from a hook in the center of the ceiling where Vinnie's most richly blossoming begonia hung in its white pot. The rough, gray plaster was almost obscured by paper and flowers. Syringas, red roses, and blue delphiniums were everywhere in crocks and vases, covering the desk, the bookcase, the window sills, even filling the stove, decorating the shelf where the water pail set and the dipper hung, and making a flowery bank behind which the speakers were to stand. So much fragrance, closed in there all night and now stirred by the breeze from the open windows, was almost overpowering.

In the midst of it all stood fifteen girls in their favorite school dresses, with their hands clasped in the folds of their skirts, and a dozen boys in clean overalls and white shirts with their hands clasped behind their backs.

Vinnie led the guests to chairs ranged along three walls, and from the corner said quietly:

"All please be seated. Lillian, who was our graduate last year, and who is now a student at Berwick Academy, will announce the numbers of our program."

Nothing more was heard from Vinnie until the end.

Lillian, a tall young girl with blonde hair in braids pinned around her head, wide blue eyes, and a soft, sweet voice, named each pupil who was to participate, gave the title of his recitation, and explained the reason for his having been chosen. The youngest lisped a four-line welcome. The winner of the spelling-down finals spoke a poem about long words. The girl who had read the greatest number of books on the approved list gave a report on *Jane Eyre*. An eight-year-old boy repeated his table of twelves. The only one to get 100 per cent on a geography examination named the forty-six states of the Union, together with their capitals and largest cities.

Here and there the program was varied by the singing of "Hail Columbia," with Lillian explaining that this music was written for the inaugural march of the first President, the father of his country, General George Washington, and of "The Battle Hymn of the Republic" and "Keller's American Hymn." The children knew all the words of all the verses, and needed neither notes nor accompaniment to sing by. Their voices rang out, and their elders joined in, Frankie's soprano as clear and true as any flute.

Toward the end of the hour Lillian introduced the two graduates of the year, her sister Martha and Hal. She said that they would give a dialogue they had first done together at the school exercises for Lincoln's birthday. Until then the audience had not noticed their absence from the room. Henry brought in and suspended two big picture frames behind the bank of flowers. The doors on either side opened, from the boys' and girls' entries, and Hal came from one end in tight pants, a black coat with tails, and a stovepipe hat, Martha from the other in a dress of watered brown silk with a big cameo at the neck, her dark hair parted in the middle and hanging in a curl behind each ear.

They took their places as portraits, motionless, silent, staring into the distance.

Then, slowly, Abraham Lincoln raised his long, bony hand and spoke, and Mary Todd Lincoln turned toward him to listen and to answer.

"It is a solemn moment, Mary, when in our beloved land men are called to raise their guns against their brothers."

"I know it, Abe. But there seems no other way."

"If it be His will, may this cup yet pass from me."

"Whatever is His will will come to pass. You shall not blame yourself. I will not allow it. You do as you must."

"I blame no one, Mary. A curtain has fallen. It must be raised. But in the meantime where we are is dark as a pocket."

"The light, when it comes, will shine upon all and be glorious."

"I cannot be sure of that. There will be bitterness to delay the dawn . . . But you are right, Mary. One day the sun will rise on a firmly united country where every man is free and loves his neighbor as himself. Though I may not live to see it."

"Much that is to be we shall not see, Abe. But you build on Washington's foundation, and those yet unborn will build on yours."

"The children . . . All children are my children . . . If I could only say how precious are the children of America, how they carry our birthright in their small hands, their sticky fingers, how brave and strong and wise they must grow to be . . ."

The talk went on and gradually died away. The figures became still portraits again, but now a hand of each rested on the picture frame.

A small boy and a small girl stood before them, looking up gravely. The girl held a few daisies, the boy a marble.

"That's President Lincoln."

"They called him Old Abe."

"He wrote the Emancipation Proclamation, and freed the slaves."

"There was a war about it."

"But he kept the Union together."

"He was the greatest President. Next to Washington, that is."

"I guess she helped him. He loved her. So I love her, too."

She tucked her daisies into Mary Todd's hand, and Abe's long, bony fingers closed gently over the proffered marble.

"Now we will sing 'America,' " Lillian said.

During the singing the portraits went away, and Vinnie came forward. She stood before them, tall in her pink cambric, and said:

"We have been proud to show you the best of what we have done in our school curriculum this year. We are happy that you have been with us for our Last Day exercises. This is an especially important Last Day here, because as most of you know, but many of my pupils have not heard until now, we shall not be re-united in the fall. Not only are two going on to the Academy, but so many young children will then be entering school that the building in District Number Ten is to be reopened, and those who live in that district will go to that school. They will have a new teacher and those who come back here will have a new teacher. I am quite sure we shall miss one another, but we shall all make new friends, and life will be good for all who continue to do their best . . . But the separation of the summer vacation and the coming year has not begun yet. Today we are still together, and we are going to enjoy it. All the work has been done. Now it's recess time. Off with your shoes! School's dismissed!"

As the children bent eagerly to knotted lacings, Vinnie glanced mischievously at their guests and said, "That permission is for anyone who wants it," and several of the men made a movement toward their feet as if to take advantage of a once welcome opportunity, but then straightened, shaking their heads and grinning at one another.

One woman said aloud, "Lord, wouldn't I like to!"

But the joys of bare feet are for the young in years. Their elders have others.

Before Vinnie's pupils' shoes were all under their desks with socks tucked safely inside, the shod men and women were tramping cheerfully between the wagons and the edge of the woods, carrying ice cream freezers packed in their wooden tubs of ice, pans of homemade bread, biscuits, cake, doughnuts, baskets of ham, hard-boiled eggs, cucumber pickles, jugs of lemonade.

The schoolchildren raced past them, shouting, on their way to the swings and the teeterboards. The smaller ones ran again in circles now converging.

Cloths were spread on the grass and moss, and as the women placed the pans and baskets and uncovered them, Frankie and Grace glanced fondly at tall sons pushing a pair of tall girls in the big swing.

"Remember how it feels to get out of school for the summer, dear?"

Frankie sang softly.

Vacation time is here again, the bright time of the year;
With happy hearts and voices we hail its advent here.
The earth is full of music; from every bush and tree
Come bursts of joyous melody, filling each heart with glee,
So let us join the chorus and raise a happy song —
Vacation time is here again; we're free all summer long.

Freedom was in the air like the perfume of roses, the buzzing of bees, the song of birds, the deep tones of men's voices, the lighter notes of women, and the unintelligible, half-wild outcries of the children.

There was eating and drinking, and talk, and play, and for the most part the women sat apart from the men, the boys played apart from the girls. But they were for that all the more aware of each other.

Verd looked across to where Frankie was perched on a ledge and noticed how pink her cheeks were from the heat, how slim her ankles crossed against the stone.

Grace thought, "How Will's hair curls across his forehead!"

"Is it true, dear, Vinnie won't teach next fall?"

"Yes. Both schools will be small compared to this one. They won't need such an experienced teacher. And Vinnie seems to want a change. She's going next week to keep house for Mr. Bannister for the summer. If she likes, she'll keep on. He's got a great, handsome house, Hattie says."

"It'll be handsomer with Vinnie in it."

"I shouldn't wonder if that's what he thinks."

There is more than music, perfume, and freedom in June. There is the tinkle of little golden chains.

"Want to swing?" Hal asked Martha. "Your — sister wants to swing with you?"

They slid silently onto the wide board and grasped the ropes. As he pushed, a hard hand against their backs to send them out, skirts flying, and waited for them to come back to him, he was glad for the first time that he would be traveling with them the four miles to the Academy and the four miles back every school day. He had a bicycle, of course. They had no bicycles. Lillian had been walking alone this year. Now Martha would walk with her. But he could be as near as he wished, on his bicycle. And when he wanted to, he could walk with them, pushing the bicycle alongside. Or even take one of them on his handlebars. He wondered which one of them it would be. Lillian was older than he, but Lillian had blonde hair. He liked blonde hair for a girl. His own was dark.

The men were loading the freezers into the wagons, the women packing baskets and folding cloths.

"Time to lower the flag, boys and girls," called Vinnie.

"Let the old cat die, Hal," sang Martha.

The swing moved slower and slower.

"You may let down the rope, Hal," said Vinnie. "And Martha may fold. The others will have turns next year." She handed the canvas bag to Martha from the doorway. "But first the pledge."

Her pupils stood in rows, the boys at salute, the girls with their hands on their hearts, all looking up.

I pledge allegiance to the flag and to the Republic for which it stands, one nation, indivisible, with liberty and justice for all.

A few minutes later everyone had gone. Vinnie, hatted and gloved, turned the key in the schoolhouse door for the last time, and walked with Mark Bannister to his automobile by the pasture bars.

JULY

JULY is the beginning of the year's prime of life. She has appeared bride at church. Her husband has opened the door of his home to her and carried in her trunk on his shoulder. From it she has taken a fringed linen cloth for their table, hemstitched sheets for their bed, crisp new roller towels to hang beside the sink, and a bright braided rug for the parlor. She has learned how hard the water is, how much soap is needed to soften it, and she has made friends with the stove. All her childhood problems are now solved, all her childish fears proved groundless. The girl has become a woman, capable and secure, and holds her future confidently in strong brown hands.

The daisies turn to gold and grow large, watching her with warm, dark eyes as she runs through the field and orchard. Summer Sweetings, red and white speckled Snowflake apples, and Striped Porters fall ripe into her looped apron. Raspberries hanging red over every rock-pile reach out to her, and the strip lots are carpeted in blue. Lettuce, radishes, and cucumbers are for the picking, and pea pods are full.

The long days roll by on greased axles, laden with tall grass new-cut and drying in the sun, the corn knee-high and ready for hoeing, potatoes, squashes, and pumpkins in bloom, sweet peas climbing up chicken wire to cover the shed wall with pink, white, red and lavender, pond lilies starring every spring-fed pool of water and filling a washtub under the dooryard tree. The nights are short and the dark is thin and soft, a-twinkle with fireflies, heavy with the heat of the sun which has scarcely gone down when the east begins to brighten, and rich with the smell of fruit and flowers and swamp and the sea on the other side of the mountain.

There is no end to the work to be done or to the pleasures to be enjoyed, no limit to the variety of both, and one slides so smoothly into the other that there is time and energy enough for all. Indeed, for July, time seems almost to stand still, and is measured, if at all, in days rather than in hours. The pendulum moves so slowly that if you watch it you grow sleepy, as if under a spell, and to sleep while the sun is up is unthinkable; it is lost opportunity.

The first service of the year in our neighborhood church is on the first Sunday of July. Through July and August, Elder Knight, who preaches every Sunday morning at his own church three miles up the road and works as a carpenter through the week and is a school committeeman, comes to us on Sunday afternoons.

The first church Sunday makes a deep impression on the neighborhood, especially on the children. In the

morning the women and children bathe in flowered
washbowls in their bedrooms; the men and boys have
taken soap and towels to the river the night before.
There is an early, cold dinner of last night's baked beans
and brown bread, curly Boston lettuce dressed in vinegar, sugar, and salt, berry pie, and lemonade. Then
the men go to put on suits, white shirts and ties, groan-
ing in exasperation when collar buttons roll under bu-
reaus and cuff links rebel against big unaccustomed
fingers trying to force them through small holes sealed
by starch. There are calls for help and for whisk
brooms to brush lint from coats and dust from hats,
and often there is no answer, for women are busy
dressing children and changing from their own wrappers
into thin, lacy, flowered, ruffled gowns.

"You'd *think*," Frankie told Marcy, "your *father*
could manage to dress himself!"

But she ran across the hall to take the whisk broom
from the hook on the closet door where it always hangs
and put it in his hand, remembering that Verd went to
church mostly for her sake and that his sister Vinnie
had told her when she first came here to live, "It's like
rigging a ship to get Verd ready to go anywhere. He has
to have everything and have it just so, and he never
knows where any of it is!"

There is always the ride in the democrat wagon up the
sandy road behind Old Bell, who wears a brown netting
with a ball fringe to keep off the flies. It has holes for
her ears, so they are not covered, and they twitch. Marcy
rides between her father and grandfather on the front
seat; her mother and Hal are on the back. When Old Bell

stops at the fence behind the church, Verd lifts Marcy out and gives his hand to Frankie, who smiles at him as she steps down. She shakes out her skirt and smooths Marcy's curls, and they all go slowly to the front of the church. Other wagons are driving up, people are walking down the road and climbing the stepping stones set into the bank.

They are very quiet. The whole world is quiet. They all go quietly through the open doors and find their places in the family pews, which are of pine with walnut railings. The women painted the pews pale green last spring and are pleased with the effect. The walls and arched ceiling are of plaster and there are oil lamps in gilded iron brackets by each window and in a five-armed gilded iron chandelier in the center, though no one is ever in the church at night unless revivalists come for a week of evening meetings.

The pews are bare and the floor is bare. Still it is very quiet, for people walk in as much on tiptoe as is possible on thick-soled shoes and sit as still as they can. You hear the ticking of the clock on the wall, and hymnbook leaves on the organ rustling in a breeze from the open windows. You smell the hymnbooks and the Sunday School books on the shelves in the corner and the big leather-bound Bible on the pulpit, and you smell the sweet peas among the baby's breath in cloudy green vases on the corners of the platform.

You know Elder Knight is on the platform, but he is almost hidden by the pulpit until he comes to it and leans across it with his forearm and hand resting lovingly on the big Bible, his long fingers touching the faded red and gold satin ribbons which mark his places in the Scriptures.

He is a tall, broad-shouldered man in a black coat and embroidered white waistcoat with the gold chain of his watch looped across it. He has a long, brown face with pink in the cheeks. His eyes are intensely blue and his hair and pointed beard are white. He is old but he looks young. He is ageless.

"Dear friends," he says, "let us lift our voices and hearts toward God by singing the Doxology."

His voice is infinitely kind. Lula Hasty moves from the front pew to the stool, her small feet press the pedals, her slender fingers pull out stops and press keys, and the reeds tremble.

> *Praise God from who all blessings flow,*
> *Praise Him all creatures here below —*

Marcy's grandmother, Bernice's grandmother, and Frankie and Grace sing soprano. Lula at the organ sings a strong alto. The Hoopers on the left, the Bostons on the right . . .

Marcy and Bernice, small creatures here below, look up at the Elder and see a soft circle of light behind his head, as Frankie and Grace and Lula did when they were small, as our children always do.

The whole service that first Sunday of last July was as our first services always are, through the hymns, the prayer, the Scripture reading, the sermon, the benediction, and that precious, that almost sacred time after the benediction when the Elder comes slowly down the pulpit steps and mingles with his people, shaking hands first with Lula — "These fingers could bring melody from stone, my child" — then with her mother and Aunt Em in their widow's crisp black dresses and sheer black silk coats and gloves and fans — "Beautiful afternoon, Sister Emma; glad to see you out, Sister Louise; they tell me you have been ill; I know you have had a hard winter, but the day is coming when there will be no more sorrow" — and then, standing beside the aisle, with everyone who passes him, a personal word for each, from the men to whom he speaks of the good weather for the haying to the infant whose cheek he touches saying, "Blessed be the little ones."

But during the Sunday School session which followed, with the Elder in the far corner teaching the Bible Class of older men and women, the teachers of the young had some difficulty in holding the attention of their pupils to the quarterlies, the story papers, the bright-pictured cards, and the reading of Bible verses to be memorized for the next Sunday; and after the singing of "Jesus loves me, this I know, for the Bible tells me so," fewer children than usual stopped to borrow books from the library. And the teachers knew why and did not insist beyond reason.

The next day was the Fourth.

Though there could be no celebration even of this great national holiday until after midnight — and after midnight they would all be asleep for some hours — every boy had packages of red firecrackers to re-count as soon as he reached home, a few had Roman candles to check on, and all had toy pistols and paper caps, torpedoes (each in a twist of tissue paper), boxes of sparklers and slow matches to count and handle and smell in proper Sunday quiet but with eager anticipation of great excitement soon to come.

" 'The pig he slept in the parlor the night before the Fourth,' " sang Hal, emptying a bucket of swill into the hogs' trough.

"They don't, really," said Marcy, standing on the lowest board of the hogs' pen fence and peering over the top at the four big pigs, the enormous sow lying on her side in the mud and the litter of seven little pigs taking their food from her with clucking, sucking noises. She thought of the parlor which had also been Vinnie's bedroom and now was the guest room, its flowered carpet swept clean with wet, shredded newspaper, the shades drawn to keep out the sun, the white lace curtains, the red plush sofa and chairs, the brass bed with the pieced velvet quilt, and the marble-topped table holding a brass lamp with a green shade, the Hasty family Bible, and Whittier bound in watered silk. What a place for pigs to be! Why would they want to? "There's no way they could get out of here and in there, *so!* Why is it always muddy where pigs are?"

"Because they make it muddy. They root," Hal answered cheerfully. "We keep moving the pen onto green grass and in twenty-four hours they've rooted it up and are in mud again. That's pigs for you ... I guess they couldn't get into parlors very well unless somebody put them there. But funny things happen the night before the Fourth. People play tricks. You can't tell. Henry and I or Leslie and Clyde and I might take it into our heads to put some pigs into some parlors to-night.''

''I guess,'' said Marcy, ''you'd get your comeuppance if you did.''

Hal laughed.

''You just look when you come downstairs tomorrow morning,'' he said. ''You just open the parlor door and look in there, that's all!''

''You'd say 'April Fool'!''

''Nobody says 'April Fool' on the Fourth of July. I'll bet you don't even know what the Fourth of July *is*.''

''Course I do. It's Independence Day. It's when they signed the Declaration. I even know who signed it.''

''Who?''

''John Hancock.''

''He wasn't the only one.''

''I know *that*. But he wrote the biggest. His name was the one I could read.''

The celebrating started earlier than any of us had expected, even Hal, who went to sleep expecting to be awakened just before daybreak by Henry's whistle under his window. Instead he was awakened a little after midnight by Ray Benson climbing into his bed. At the same time Marcy rolled over against the wall of her alcove in response to pushes and muttering and felt someone hot and fat and cross roll into the narrow cot beside her. Even when she woke in the morning and hastily crawled out around her bedfellow she did not know who it was.

Frankie had been roused from the first sweet sleep of

the summer night by the motor of an automobile chugging up the lane, by its lights turning into the yard, and then by squawks of the horn and a woman's voice calling, "Frankie! Frankie Hasty! Come down here! If you don't come out and treat us right, we'll be troublesome all night!"

This is a shout customary at serenades of newly married couples, and a man began to sing.

> *Down by the old mill stream*
> *Where I first met you*
> *With your eyes so blue,*
> *Dressed in gingham, too —*

What in the dear Lord's world!

Frankie pulled a wrapper over her nightgown, wondering how Verd could sleep through that, knowing well enough his father wouldn't, and ran down the dark front stairs, lit a lamp, and went to the screen door.

"Oh, you're took, Frankie!" called the woman's voice. "You're took tonight!"

People were getting out of the automobile. Its lights went off. They stumbled up the steps, and Frankie recognized the Bensons, Jack and Pauline who had lived next door in Rochester, their boy, who was Hal's age but bigger and older-looking than Hal, and Gertrude, who was born two months before Marcy. The boys had played together in Rochester, and Frankie and Pauline had sometimes walked together along the street, pushing their baby carriages. But that all seemed long ago and unlikely now. And there was a girl with them Frankie had never seen before; perhaps fourteen or fifteen years old.

"Well, Pauline! Jack! What are you doing out here this time of night? You lost?"

Oh, no, they weren't lost. They were on their way to spend the Fourth at the beach. Jack had just bought the automobile on Saturday and they had been out riding around in it all day and evening, took such a big picnic lunch some of it was still left. It was such a hot night nobody wanted to go home.

"And being as it's the night before the Fourth and we're going to start early in the morning for the beach anyway," said Pauline, "Jack said, 'Let's head that way now and wake up the Hastys.' So here we are. This is Aggie Saunders. She's kind of Ray's sweetheart."

Sweethearts at fourteen!

"Do her folks know where she is?" asked Frankie.

"They know she's with us. They don't worry about her when she's with us; do they, Aggie? Now don't you go to any bother for us, Frankie. We've all slept on the floor before and can again."

But nobody slept on the floor at Hastys'. Frankie was thankful that the brass bed in the parlor was already made up, and that Hal's was a double bed. But she was sorry for Marcy, and for Gertrude, too, that both would have to finish the night before the Fourth in one cot in a windowless alcove. She couldn't blame George for threshing about on his cornhusk mattress and clearing his throat irritably; he worked hard from four o'clock in the morning until eight o'clock at night six days a week and enjoyed every minute of it; this was no way to end his one day of rest before starting the next six. She moved as quietly as she could, opening the bed-couch in the sitting room and making it up for Aggie. But when she passed the closed parlor door there was still a rectangle of lamplight around it, and Jack and Pauline were splashing at the washbowl in water she had carried in, talking and laughing.

"They're so tired they're foolish," she thought, climbing the dark stairs. "And so am I. We're too old for such carrying on, and I know it even if they don't."

Hal and Marcy were not too old.

When Henry's pebbles struck the windowpane and he whistled, Hal leaped up, routed out the sleepy boy beside him, and five minutes later a giant firecracker went off, hurling a tin pan to the roof. Giants continued to go off, for Ray had brought a fine supply. And ten minutes later Marcy, Gertrude, and even Aggie were tossing torpedoes against the rocky bank of the lane, shooting paper caps, touching the fuses of small crackers with slow matches and then running and squealing with their fingers in their ears. Ray had so many packages of small crackers that he fired whole packages at once and they went off like a fusillade.

Their parents turned over and groaned. It had been too short a night, and the heat of the day was beginning at dawn.

But George only grunted, sat up on the side of his bed, and reached for his overalls hanging by their straps from the bedpost. Fourth of July again. The Fourth was the day to sweep the barn, the rafters and the top loft from which the haycart hung, and all the way down, with the three great doors open wide; tomorrow, if it was fair, he would mow the back field, and new hay must have a clean house. As soon as he had built the fire and put on the filled teakettle, he went to open up the barn, and by the time Verd came, yawning, the cows had been milked and turned out to pasture. They had swept the rafters when Frankie called them to breakfast; could go on to the walls and the lofts as soon as they had eaten. Before night the spare floor would be tidy as a kitchen floor, and they would let down the haycart.

The Bensons had different plans. Pauline said she wished she could help Frankie with the breakfast dishes but the tide would turn at ten o'clock and they did not want the young ones in the water when it was too far out. They all had bathing suits; Pauline's was new, with special stockings and laced blue boots to wear with it. They left the remains of yesterday's picnic for the pigs, saying they would have their dinner in a restaurant at York and go later to Hampton to see the fireworks at night, and rode out of the yard waving and calling back words nobody could understand. Jack and Pauline were in front with Gertrude between them, and Ray and Aggie were in back. The top of the automobile was folded down. Ray's good-by was his last package of firecrackers tossed, lighted, toward Hal, who had to back away.

"Well!" Frankie exclaimed. "I hope that's the last I ever see of *them*. Of all the selfish, inconsiderate people I ever came across! I'd no more do to anybody what they've done to me —"

"I'd help you with the dishes," Hal said, "but Papa told me to come to the barn —"

"Marcy and I can do the dishes. But after barging in here the way they did, the least they could have done was to ask you two to go to the beach with them. Marcy's never been to the beach but once in her life, and neither of you ever rode in an automobile. Not that I'd have let her go with that crew. But they could have *asked!*"

"Well, I wouldn't have gone," Hal said. "Seen plenty of them already. And I've got to help clean the barn for the haying."

He ran off whistling. Frankie and Marcy went slowly into the house and began clearing the littered kitchen. It was quiet everywhere. All the torpedoes, the paper caps, and the firecrackers had been exploded.

"There's nothing left of the Fourth but my box of sparklers for tonight," thought Marcy. "How could it be so near over so soon?"

But it was not nearly over. It had barely begun, and the rest was a dizzy whirl.

Marcy and her mother were still at the sink when her Aunt Vinnie rode into the yard with Mark Bannister in his automobile. But it was not the same automobile in which he had come to her Last Day of school. This one was much larger, with two big seats and a top, painted dark red with the initials M.B. in gold on the door.

Vinnie, all in white with a blue sash, came running in. Frankie cried, "Oh, Vinnie Hasty, don't you dare *look* at this house!" Vinnie took a quick glance around, laughed, and said, "What have you, had a tornado here? Give me a dish towel, and I'll tell you what we've come for. Mr. Bannister's gone to the barn to see the menfolks. I told him they'd be sweeping it out."

They had come in the big car to take as many Hastys as could go with them to the Webbers' in Eliot. George was having a great Fourth of July celebration at his place and hundreds of people from miles around were coming. It was for the benefit of some club George belonged to, and the members of it would serve dinner in tents, and supper, too, and there would be speaking in the afternoon, and fireworks at night. There was an admission charge for the public, but Hattie wanted them all to come and said it wouldn't cost them a cent; and Mr. Bannister or George Webber (who had just bought an automobile) would bring them home when it was over.

Well, George Hasty said he wouldn't go ten rods to see money blown into the sky; the best fireworks in the world was a good, ripping thunderstorm, which came free and could be watched from his own porch. Verd said he would like to go and was much obliged, but the grass was at its height and the barn must be ready. Frankie sighed and said if Verd could go she would like to, but as it was, what she wanted most was to get this house straightened out and then roll into the hammock and go to sleep. *Her* celebration was going to be putting off the washing until the next day, a self-indulgence she had never yet allowed herself on a clear Monday since she was married.

So it was arranged that Hal and Marcy would ride to

Eliot with Vinnie and Mr. Bannister and take a few things with them so that Hal could stay on for a visit with Roland Webber, his cousin, and Marcy with Vinnie at the Bannister farm.

Go away to a great celebration and stay away *all night?* Marcy could hardly believe her ears!

"What if Marcy gets homesick?" Frankie asked. "She's never slept away from home without me. I've never left her overnight except when Lula's baby died."

"There always has to be a first time," Vinnie said matter-of-factly. "There are toys for her to play with at Mr. Bannister's. Ones his children had. There's a velocipede she can ride. There's a lazy old Shetland pony too."

A velocipede! A pony!

"And any time today or tonight or any night that she says the word," Mr. Bannister told Frankie, smiling at Marcy, "we'll bring her straight home. And that's a promise."

"But if she's contented until then," added Vinnie, "we'll keep her until Sunday and then bring them both up. Or George and Hattie will."

Verd and George stood in the barn door to wave good-by to them and Frankie waved from the yard as the automobile moved away from her. Marcy was surprised to find that the three figures and even the maple trees and the house blurred as she looked back at them.

But then they were out of the lane into the main road, moving faster and faster, so fast that Marcy could not distinguish one blade of grass from another in the ditch beside her, where she sat on the back seat with Vinnie.

A strong wind was blowing full in her face, Hal turned from the front and shouted, "Say, this is — *royal*, Marcy!" and Marcy was in a new world.

They careened along roads and past houses she could not remember having seen before. Many of them had flags out, so she knew it was America. They flew over bridges, across railroad tracks, up and down hills, and laughed at their queer sensations as they went over sudden little rises which Mr. Bannister called thank-you-ma'ams. And finally they rolled into a yard which was all soft green and had a green chain fence around it. Beyond the fence there were buildings and flags and a field full of automobiles and another field full of horses and wagons and another field full of tents large and small. Around everything people were coming and going like ants at an anthill. And at the back of everything a train was going by with a rush and a roar and a rumble, puffing black smoke.

Hattie ran out of the house and kissed Hal and Marcy. George came out of a tent and shook hands with Hal, lifted Marcy out of her seat and tossed her into the air. Roland and Hal went away with Hal's box of things. Vinnie went into the house with Hattie. Marcy joined the ants and did not know which ant she was all day. She ran with packs of children who fell over pegs and ropes, crawled under tents, reached into tubs of ice water and pulled out bottles of tonic someone opened for them like magic so that they could drink as they ran, the glass clinking against their teeth. They snatched cookies from wooden boxes and fed them to horses in their stalls, lit and tossed firecrackers and ran screaming

away from them, ate salmon salad and rolls at long
tables in the biggest tent, ran out eating striped ice cream
from boxes with wooden spoons. They played croquet
and knocked split balls so far they lost them, listened
to speeches, ran to watch every train which passed,
climbed ladders. Once when Marcy climbed a ladder a
red-haired boy was right behind her, and nobody else.
At the top they were alone in the new hay. The red-
haired boy kissed Marcy and braided a hay ring for her
finger and told her his name was Arthur. Then she
heard a train coming and went down the ladder so fast
that she lost Arthur and never saw him again. But she
saw the train, and it was a freight. She counted thirty-
nine cars. It was beginning to grow dark, and they ate
again at the long tables; hot turkey sandwiches this
time, with gravy on them, and peas, and pie. Then
Vinnie and Hattie found Marcy and took her with them
to sit in Mr. Bannister's automobile and wait for the
fireworks.

They let her sit on the outside nearest where the
fireworks would go off, and that was the side next to the
broad field beside the meadow through which the railroad tracks ran. Everything below was half obscured in
soft darkness now, and strangely quiet. The men were
small black figures around the platform setting up the
display. Women and children were huddled in wagons
and automobiles and on blankets spread on hillsides.
Older boys and girls had wandered off together to pasture
pines or garden benches or fences they could lean against.
Only the sky was bright with a new moon and thousands
of stars.

Marcy looked around and up and down again and thought, "How little we are, with the sky so big."

A train came through, as she had hoped it would; a passenger train with all its windows lighted, and its whistle blowing four times, the same four notes and the last one dying away into the distance as the lighted windows vanished into the woods.

"Even a train is small," thought Marcy. "They looked big today but they're small in the night when the stars are out. I could see little people in the cars. Little people like us."

"Where are the people going?" she asked dreamily.

"What people?"

"In the cars."

"Oh, to Portland, and Bangor, and Houlton, and St. Johns, New Brunswick."

"Why?"

"Different reasons. Each one has his own reason."

"I don't see why they want to go so far away."

"Away from what?"

"From home."

Vinnie and Hattie exchanged glances. They suspected Marcy was growing homesick, but they were mistaken. She was with Vinnie and Hattie. She felt at home.

"Some of them are going home," said Vinnie. "They live there."

"I don't see why they want to live so far away."

Home now was her grandfather's farm and the Webber farm and the Bannister farm. These three were the triangle in the center of the world.

"Some of them are going visiting," said Hattie. "To stay awhile with people they love and that love them." She patted Marcy's white stocking-covered knee.

"We're all little," thought Marcy. "Like toys. But we're not toys. We do things without people making us. We plan it up ourselves, and then we do it. Some people are good and some people are bad. But we all better be smart, and we all better be brave. Because we're so little."

The first Roman candles went off, three low arcs of flame. Then skyrockets at a slant, rising well above the tree line before they went out in showers of little stars. After that Roman candles and skyrockets kept going off for an hour, and every few minutes a set piece went up higher than candles or rockets and hung there briefly, making patterns like those at the end of a kaleidoscope or like a tree strung with colored lights or like a sparkling vase full of blue and red and yellow flowers. As each of these patterns took shape there was a low chorus of "Oh-h-h-h!" which ran over the whole Webber farm like a row of dominoes falling in the dark.

At last a man's voice — George Webber's — announced from the platform, "The final piece is about to go up, neighbors! We have celebrated again the signing of the Declaration of Independence. All stand, and sing 'The Star-Spangled Banner.' Fred Place will lead us."

There was a rising movement everywhere, in the wagons and automobiles, on the hillsides, in garden and pasture, and along the fences.

O say, can you see, by the dawn's early light,
What so proudly we hailed at the twilight's last
gleaming?

A puff of light. An explosion.

Whose broad stripes and bright stars, through the
perilous fight,
O'er the ramparts we watched, were so gallantly
streaming!

And there it was! Coming together, red and white stripes, blue field and white stars . . .

And the rockets' red glare, the bombs bursting in
air,
Gave proof through the night that our flag was
still there.

Not only there but waving proudly as if in a strong wind . . .

'Tis the star-spangled banner! O long may it
wave
O'er the land of the free and the home of the
brave!

And before it went out, a golden rectangle formed about it like a frame, like a wall, like a fortress to guard it through the night . . .

Riding between Vinnie and Mr. Bannister, Marcy said, "I wonder if they could see it."

"Don't see how anybody could miss it," Mr. Bannister answered, "who wasn't asleep. I didn't know but you would be asleep by the end, Marcy. You've had quite a day."

But Vinnie knew Marcy.

"If who could see it?" she asked.

"The stars. And the angels. Anybody but us and God. We didn't get it very high. But we got it as high as we could. If they could see it, they know which flag is ours. They know we're America."

"We can't tell," Vinnie answered. "But we know they will see it if we get it high enough, so we'll keep on trying to get it higher. And there are other ways of trying to get it higher than shooting it into the sky."

"What other ways?"

"Making freedom count. Showing what it can do. Growing and loving and studying and building. Being all that free men and women can be. We'll talk about it tomorrow."

Marcy was asleep when they reached the Bannister farm, and Mr. Bannister carried her up to Vinnie's room and laid her on Vinnie's bed.

From the doorway he asked, "How much do you think she understands when you talk to her like that?"

"I don't know," Vinnie answered, opening Marcy's box. "Any more than I know whether 'the stars and the angels' could see George's fireworks. But if we didn't talk to her like that, how would she *ever* understand it? I've always believed that whatever you tell children often enough gets through to them, sooner or later. To some of them sooner and other ones later.''

"Too bad you don't have children of your own, Miss Hasty.''

Vinnie smiled, shaking out Marcy's white nainsook nightgown.

"I have hundreds,'' she said, "and even the big ones like to get back under my wing once in a while.''

AUGUST

AUGUST is a matron, full-breasted, broad-hipped, resting on her doorstep in the afternoon, wearing a clean, pale yellow apron over her berry-stained dress. The muggy heat has twisted her short hairs into damp curls around her face and there are beads of perspiration on her upper lip, but the fingers which move her palm-leaf fan are dry. She looks off over her husband's fields where the second crop of grass is rising on the high ground even as he rides the mowing machine in the meadow or clips out with his scythe along the stone walls and under the fences, and where the corn hangs heavy, new potatoes are setting on, purplish pumpkins are the size of a baby's head, and yellow seed cucumbers are ready for pickling; but a haze half obscures it all.

A haze half obscures her thoughts, too, her memories, her knowledge of duty done and undone, her time sense.

A week ago, it seems, she was a child naked between rough home-spun sheets in the step-bedroom off her grandmother's kitchen, drowsily listening to the brook as it ran cool under the window. Day before yesterday she was a girl standing barefoot on a lonely beach, picking up the clams a tall boy dug, and tingling when his hand touched hers as they carried home the basket together. Yesterday she had a houseful of children always hungry, always needing their necks scrubbed, their hair braided, their stomachs rubbed, their bottoms spanked, their britches patched, their shoes resoled. Where are they now? And who are all those lusty young men and women who come in the evenings or on Sundays, carrying and leading and scolding children of their own? Where is the child who heard the brook? Where is the girl who picked up the clams? Where is the boy who dug them? And who is the woman sitting on the doorstep? Who is the man on the mowing machine?

No matter.

August is hot. Opulent, tired, thirsty, hot, in a clean apron over a work-stained dress. She is so full of earthy wisdom that she knows all she needs to know or ever will, and has nothing more to learn. She asks no questions about the purpose of life, is heavy with answers as a cow with milk coming up the pasture lane at day's end. A child is to play and get into mischief and do his chores and eat and sleep and grow. A girl is to be found by a boy on a beach or in an orchard or by the railing of a bridge where he can carve their initials. A woman is to know a man, to know him and stay by him both by day and by night, to keep his house and bear his children and then to feed and warm and love and discipline them all as long as they are within her reach.

August is the meeting place of the currents of the

year. She feels the meeting within her, the waters from many directions surging into a mighty eddy; but she is not shaken by it, encompasses it calmly as she carried her children to full term despite their struggles to find a way out of the pocket in which she held them until it was time for them to go. She is even faintly amused by the surging and eddying, as she was by the struggles of her unborn.

"Don't be in such a hurry," she used to mutter. "You'll get there soon enough. And likely wish you was back."

Her blue-black eyes, deep in their sockets, shine. She looks about her at what she can see of the world into which the great river of the year will flow when it leaves her, and wonders what barriers it will crash against, whether it will go through, over, or around them, and how gracefully it will wear an armor of ice. But she cannot see far, for the haze.

No matter. The river, once loosed, must make its own bed, take its own course. She is the here and now.

Her man will soon be in from the field, and his house is ready for him. Window sills lined with ripening tomatoes. Many shelves filled with many glass jars of green vegetables and fruit. A blackberry pie on the back of the stove ready to be topped with white of egg and lightly browned in the oven . . .

Last August we had a long, dry spell and one after another the wells failed. Ours did not fail entirely, and for a week or more all the neighbors took their drinking water from it, boys coming with buckets by day and men with tubs in their wagons at night. But when it ran dark with sediment from the spout and had a strange taste, men dug out a living spring by the riverbank to the size of a barrel and we all had our drinking water from that. One evening Verd made a small yoke of pine to fit Hal's thin neck and narrow shoulders, with rope at the ends and hooks where he could hang the pails. Verd said it would be much easier for Hal than carrying the full pails so far in his hands, and he sandpapered the half-collar and rubbed it with beeswax; but still Frankie looked at it with a feeling like horror, remembering pictures she had seen of slave water-carriers. She thought Hal did enough, raking after the hayloads and helping to stow them away in the loft, keeping the weeds out of his beets and carrots and hoeing his potatoes, riding his bicycle in the evenings to deliver copies of the *Utica Saturday Globe* and to sell wall mottoes. But the planted piece and the selling were to earn money for his education, quite apart from the haying and the bringing of wood and water which were his contribution to the family, in a way a small return for his room and board.

Frankie began to put frosting on the cakes she made for him and kept in the tank of the kitchen stove, which was not heated in summer when she used another in the shedroom for cooking. A cake in the tank stayed moist, and was protected from flies and the tiny red ants which flow in ruddy streams into the cellar at this time of year.

Laundry waited to be done, and mounted — wet pieces having been pinned dirty to the lines to dry so that they would not mildew — until baskets spilled over and women grew desperate, especially Frankie, who until now had always had clean underclothes, shirt, and socks ready for Verd every summer morning of their married life.

"What in the dear Lord's world am I going to do?" she asked Vinnie, who had come home for a few days while Mr. Bannister was on a visit to his married daughter in New York. "I can't — *won't* — have Hal lug enough water so far for a wash like that, and Verd and Father and Old Bell have all they can do in the hayfield, rushing now the way they are because the grass is drying up so fast and Verd's work is piling up at the shop."

"Well, three ways we could do," said Vinnie. "Let Hal bring enough water for the pieces you need most. Or let everything go a few more days in hopes they'll be through haying and Verd can haul you a hogsheadful. Or take the wash to the water — and *that's* what *I'd* do."

So that was what they did. Marcy coo-hooed Bernice to the riverbank and told her that was what they were going to do. Bernice ran home and told her mother. Grace thought that was a good idea, and said she would do the same.

Early next morning Hasty and Dorr men, on a roundabout way to the fields, carried benches and tubs and washboards to the river's edge. A half hour later, breakfast dishes done, beds stripped, and cold dinner for the men under cheesecloth on the kitchen tables, women and children followed, with high-piled baskets, lard pails of soft soap made by slicing yellow bars into hot water to set overnight, and their lunch in tin boxes and glass bottles.

For Marcy and Bernice this was a storybook come to life. It combined all the qualities they liked best in stories; the lovely unreality of fairy tales, the earthiness of fables, and the shared ecstasy of poor little rich city children set free on a country holiday.

"Wonder what old Mr. Sun thinks to see us here," said Vinnie. "Maybe he thinks he must have taken a wrong turn and is over India."

Though there were only three women — two on one bank and one on the other — the river seemed to be lined with women on both sides, all in big straw hats, with their skirts pinned high and their sleeves rolled up, some dipping water, some already scrubbing sturdily at their washboards, some calling back and forth, some singing as they worked. As soon as a towel or a sheet was clean and rinsed, it was spread on the grass to bleach. White shirts and underwear were hung on bushes. The meadow had become a house without walls.

The children, scrambling along the steep banks through the skunk cabbage, asked, "Can we paddle, Mama? It isn't deep! The water only comes up to my wrist!"

"Yes. I know it's low. Take off your tiers and keep close to the edge. It may still be over your heads in the middle."

But it wasn't. The motion of what water there was was sluggish, and Marcy and Bernice in white pants buttoned to white Ferris waists waded closer and closer to each other until they clasped hands, and a minute later were together on Grace's side of the river.

"See me, Mama! Auntie!" cried Marcy. "See where I am!"

It was as if she and Bernice had scaled the walls of a fort, or climbed the Jungfrau, or crossed the Hellespont.

As far as they knew, they were the first ever to have forded the river.

"My goodness," Grace called. "Who would have thought it could get that low? They hardly wet the lace on their drawers."

"Out west," said Vinnie, "the smaller rivers dry up entirely every summer. They say the bottom of the river beds is dusty."

"I don't think I could live long where I couldn't see water," Frankie said. "How I long to get to the beach, nobody knows! Every summer I wait in hope — and this is the third one in a row that I haven't seen the ocean nor even smelled it except in a sea turn."

But the children longed for nothing they did not have. They crossed and recrossed the river, slipping on the sleek stones, feeling the mud ooze between their toes. They built mud houses at the water's edge and thought mice would live in them, caught a small fish and let him go, found river clam shells and stacked them like plates under a birch tree. They had left their tiers on the Hasty side, and did not put them on until they had washed off the mud and dried themselves in the sun and it was time to come up to the meadow for lunch.

Bernice had already brought over her and her mother's lunch, and now Grace had taken off her shoes and stockings and was wading across with skirt lifted, catching her breath and letting out a little cry when a misstep halfway across threatened to seat her in midcurrent.

But she came up the bank laughing, and they all sat in a shady corner of the room without walls, now hung lavishly in color as well as in white, to eat hungrily of sour milk biscuits, crisp slices of salt pork, hard-boiled eggs and strips of cucumber dipped in salt and pepper, early sweet apples and doughnuts. Frankie and Grace — because they were Brookses — had brought cold tea to drink, but Vinnie and the girls had bottles of the root beer Frankie had mixed in great kettles and poured into the bottles to be sealed with snap-down metal covers and kept in a warm place for three days and nights to ferment before it was ready to be cooled for drinking.

While the women were eating they talked, and when they had finished eating they talked more, a little of washing and cooking and root-beer-making, but mostly of what they remembered or each hoped the others would help her to remember.

"I was trying to think the other day — whatever become of that Sarah Chadbourne that stayed on at the old Neale place with her little young ones after her husband died, that Vest Chadbourne that was the schoolmaster?"

"You don't remember her, do you, Grace?"

"No, but the old ones used to tell about her. How she was a little slim thing who never lived on a farm before, but there she was alone with three mouths to feed and she went into the field brave as a man —"

"Father's spoken of her. He knew her. He went to school to Vest, you know. Sarah went out to Williamstown to live, finally. Vest's brother Paul was president of a college out there. I think his wife died and Sarah kept house for him."

Marcy and Bernice half-listened, half-drowsed, flat on smooth brown pine spills, looking up into dark branches. It was all so peaceful. The air was fresh with the smell of pine and river and sweet grass and sweet fern and clean clothes, and the women were talking, smoothing and folding as they talked . . .

But, "Well, *my* clean clothes are still hanging on the other side. I guess Grammy Dorr'll fold for us when we get them home, won't she, Bernice?"

"We'd better take the sheets and pillowcases and get them back onto the beds. What has to be ironed I'm going to leave here; Verd can get them when he comes for the tubs and bench, after the dew falls. So they'll be just right to iron in the morning. Marcy, you can carry the pail of socks."

So the outing was over. The Hastys watched until the Dorrs were safely back to their side of the river, and everyone moved slowly, burdened with clean linen, toward home. But Marcy, looking over her shoulder at the empty room without walls, knew that she would never again see it as a meadow.

"Now, Frank," Vinnie was saying from her end of the long basket, "Father said this morning what hay was out would be in by tonight, and he wasn't going to mow any more for a few days because it wouldn't hurt the grass in the rest of the low ground to wait and he had another job on his mind; said Verd ought to get down to the shop to look after his business, too. So why don't you have him take you up to spend tomorrow with your mother and Lula? Make a little change for you. I'll be here to get meals and see to Marcy and the ironing. Just as soon do it as not. Fact is, I'd like to. You could even stay overnight if you want to. Mr. Bannister won't come for me before the end of the week.''

''Why, I'd never thought of such a thing, Vinnie.''
But she thought of it now, of her mother's voice and
Lula's laughter, of her mother's bread and Lula's sponge
cake and tapioca pudding, of how when she was there
at night the three sat around the kitchen table to sing as
soon as the supper dishes were done, and then for
hours after Clarence had gone to bed her mother read
aloud, knitting as she read, while Lula and Frankie
sewed. ''I suppose I could, couldn't I? I'll talk it over
with Verd tonight.''

She did not feel guilty in accepting Vinnie's offer
because she knew it was true that Vinnie would enjoy
being alone with Hastys, exactly as Frankie would enjoy
a long day and a long evening alone with Brookses. It
is like a drink from a fountain of youth to go back for a
little while to the rooftree of one's parent and one's
sister or brother. There is a tempo there, a cadence, to
which a woman is forever fitted and into which she slips
effortlessly to rest and be renewed.

They were turning into the yard now and Vinnie
exclaimed, ''Well, *what's* going on *here?*''

The pump was out of the well, lying in the edge of
the field. Around the well, field stones were piled and
they were splashed with mud. George Hasty's head was
just appearing out of the well as he climbed a ladder
protruding from it.

''What's happened, Father?'' Frankie cried. ''Has it
gone bone-dry?''

''No,'' he answered, ''Tain't bone-dry. But it's only
got two feet of water in it. Measured it last night and

[156]

before morning I'd made up my mind to lower this well ten feet before I done another thing. Verd and Hal's getting in the hay today. I been digging here, and will be till I've got this well so that as long as anybody lives on this place they'll never again be plagued by drouth.''

Never again be plagued by drouth . . .

"Oh, my,'' breathed Frankie. "But, Father, you ought not to be down there alone. What if the sides should cave in? What if the stones should fall on you and break an arm or a leg? What if the water should come rushing in so fast you couldn't get out in time?''

" 'Twun't,'' said George.

He emptied a bucket of mud he had brought up with him, filled the bucket with stones and lowered it, and went down the ladder again.

"Had he ought to, Vinnie? Shouldn't somebody younger —''

"They come younger,'' said Vinnie, "but they don't come better for a job like digging and stoning up a well. He's done it before. He knows just how. Go make your beds. I'll start the supper. They'll all be hungry when they come in tonight.''

Marcy slept with Vinnie that night, and before she woke in the morning her father had taken her mother to the house George's brother Joe built and in which Joe's son, Clarence, now lives with his wife, Lula, and her mother Louise Emery, who are Frankie's sister and mother.

"They'll have a great time,'' Vinnie told Marcy. "I expect they'll rake the woods for blackberries as soon as the wet is off. You know how they all like to pick.

Well, we'll have a good time, too. After we get the dishes done I'm going to make green-apple pies, and I'll bake some little ones in saucers. You can bring out the hats and boxes of trimmings from behind the curtain in my room, if you want to, and see how good a milliner you are. This afternoon we'll invite the dolls to tea on the porch and have the saucer pies and pink lemonade.''

But Frankie and Lula were not blackberrying. Frankie had hardly stepped down from Verd's wagon when Lula asked her how she would like to go to the beach for the day. Lula could have the horse, for Clarence had finished his haying. They could take a lunch and go over the New Road around the mountain, be in sight of the water by eleven o'clock, and just sit and watch the waves as long as they wanted to, right up until dark if they wanted to, for Lula was not afraid to drive through the woods after dark. Lula is not afraid of anything.

''Why, I don't know as I ought to say it, Lula, but it's like an answer to prayer. There's nothing in this world I'd like so much to do as go to the beach. I don't know, I've been just *longing* —''

All day they were like two children playing truant. Riding off through the trees, along the narrow, rocky road, they left problems, anxiety, and grief behind them with a delicious sense of abandon, of mischief bordering on wickedness, of dancing with no money jingling in their pockets for the piper.

All day they talked. Past old stone walls; past the Norman farm surrounded by woods, where Lula waved to a boy who walked out past her house every day to school; into the shadow of Hedgehog Rocks, over the foothills of Mount Agamenticus, and down the other side; through miles and miles of wilderness, they talked. At last, around a curve on a high point, they could look down the straight road bordered by trees as through a spyglass and see the white summer hotels, the gray fishermen's cottages, and the sand dunes of Ogunquit. Beyond these the water ran out to touch the sky.

"There's the ocean," cried Frankie, drawing a deep breath. She repeated softly, "There's the ocean."

"Yes, siree," laughed Lula, "there's the ocean. And, you know, I do believe it's been there all the time!"

They hitched the horse at a granite post in the shade near the post office, Lula put on his feed bag, and they talked while he ate. He had had a long drink at a brook coming down from the mountain. Then they took their lunch pails from the back of the wagon and walked, almost running, down to the dunes. Lula did stop on the way to buy a paper bag of cherries and two bottles of ginger ale. The storekeeper lent her a bottle opener to take along.

Alone with the dunes and the sea they took off their shoes and stockings, waded like children in warm pools left from high tide, finally ventured a little way into the sparkling waves, and afterward sat on lobster crates and ate their lunch, drank their warm ginger ale, exclaiming, "Look! Look! There comes a big one! . . . Now watch. Count. They say every seventh —"

All afternoon and early evening they walked the beach, picking up shells to take home, filling their lunch pails with sand to take home, talking. They lay among the dunes, resting, talking. They climbed to the top of the highest dune and watched the reflection in the eastern sky, and on the water, of a brilliant sunset. They spoke of others who would like to be there with them, and wished they were, yet admitted their own joy that only they were there, for once alone together.

"I suppose we ought to be ashamed," said Frankie.

"I'm not," Lula replied stoutly. "When did it ever happen before? Or will it again? We spend most of our lives, late years, doing for the rest of them. Today is our turn. Let's make the most of it."

They did. At dusk they turned slowly away from the sea, put on their shoes and stockings, picked up their shells and pails of sand, and walked quietly back to where the horse was hitched.

The streetlamps of the little village had been turned on. The post office and the drugstore were open, flooded with electric light. It was as Frankie and Lula imagined Broadway in New York City — a Gay White Way, with couples promenading, the ladies all in white and plumes on their hats, the gentlemen long-legged in tight pants and short jackets, checkered vests, and derbies.

Lula took the feed bag from under the wagon seat and filled it with oats from a wooden measure.

"While he's eating," said Frankie suddenly, "you and I are going into the drugstore and have ice cream sodas. I haven't tasted one since we left Rochester."

They sat at a small round table with a marble top, and there was white light all around them. Lula's soda was strawberry with strawberry ice cream; pink as rose petals. Frankie's was sarsaparilla with vanilla ice cream.

They drew cold sweetness through long straws and dipped it with long-handled spoons, and this was bliss after the heat of the day and the salt of the air.

When they came out it was dark, but they were not much aware of the darkness until they left the village behind and headed into the woods toward the black shape of the mountain. Then they began to sing.

First they sang happy songs . . . "In the Shade of the Old Apple Tree," "Meet Me in St. Louis, Louis," "In the Good Old Summertime," "Daisy, Daisy, Give Me Your Answer, Do," "Little Annie Rooney," "She'll Be Comin' Round the Mountain," "Yankee Doodle Dandy," "The Wabash Cannon Ball."

As the darkness closed in all around so that they could no longer see road or horse or even each other, but only a narrow ribbon of distant stars where the road ahead cut through the blanket of trees, and the horse was finding his own way over the ledges, they sang sad, sweet songs . . . "On the Trail of the Lonesome Pine," "Juanita," "Redwing," "Silver Bell," "Evelina," "Seeing Nelly Home," "The Vacant Chair," "Grandfather's Clock," "Listen to the Mocking Bird," "I'm Tying the Leaves So They Won't Come Down," "Young Charlotte," "Darling Nelly Gray," "Swanee River," "My Bonnie Lies Over the Ocean," "Old Dog Tray."

As time passed in the darkness until they lost all sense of it or of distance, and did not know where they were except that the steel rims of the wheels were still scraping rock, they began to sing hymns . . . "The Old Rugged Cross," "I Love to Tell the Story," "Work, for the Night Is Coming," "Safe in the Arms of Jesus," "All

the Way My Savior Leads Me," "Fully Persuaded,"
"There Shall Be Showers of Blessings," "The Lily of
the Valley," "It Is Well with My Soul," "Bringing
in the Sheaves."

Suddenly Lula said, "Funny. Seems as if I smell
smoke!"

Frankie sniffed and almost thought she did, too.

They were quiet after that, wondering, until they
reached the Hedgehog Rocks. There they could see the
wall of stone beside them in a faint light which came
from below, on the left, where in the thick black a fire
was burning. It looked small, from this distance, but
across the distance they could hear it crackle.

"Swamp pickers," said Lula. "Either dropped a
match that smoldered, or knocked out a pipe with a live
ash in it."

"And the woods a tinderbox," said Frankie. "Wonder
if anybody else has seen it. Not likely; it's so far from
anywhere but Normans' and they've probably been abed
and asleep for hours."

"I'll get them up," said Lula. "Next thing I do.
No time to lose."

"It's lucky there's no wind."

"One may come up with the sun."

It was not far to Normans'. The buildings were dark.

Lula shouted, "Wake up! Wake up! Fire at the edge
of the swamp below Hedgehow Rocks! Wake up!"

A sleepy man's voice through an upstairs window
asked, "Huh? Who's that? What say?"

"It's Lula Hasty. On the way home from Ogunquit.
Saw the fire when we rounded Hedgehog Rocks. Better

get over there as fast as you can. I'll get Clarence and the rest of the men on York Road to come right over.''

They plunged out of the small clearing and into the woods again. But everything had changed now. An idyl had ended. They were springing into action. The piper must be paid.

Lula hurried the horse as much as he would be hurried. He was of no mind to break a leg on a rolling stone or by stepping into a hole.

''Can you take me home as soon as you get Clarence started?'' Frankie asked. ''Then we can tell Verd and he'll get a crew together from down our way.''

''That's what I thought I would. Uncle George will be worried. You know that fire's not far from his McIntire lot.''

She calls George Hasty ''Uncle George'' because he is Clarence's uncle.

''The best lot he owns,'' said Frankie. ''If it isn't stopped before it gets into that, I don't know as they can stop it anywhere.''

''Here we are,'' Lula said. ''Hold the reins.''

She was back in a few minutes with Frankie's suitcase.

''Get up, Prince; hurry up now. Clarence is running down to tell Uncle Gran and Charles and Ralph. I'll stop a minute to rouse Len.''

It was twenty minutes after midnight when Lula and Frankie drove into our dooryard. Five minutes later Lula was driving out with Hal beside her because Frankie did not want her to travel alone. Verd and George would pick him up at her house on their way into the woods. At half-past twelve Verd was in his gig behind Bess, racing through the night to wake Bennie and Henry, George Earle and George Goodwin, Oliver and Peter, and the four Dorr men and boys. By one o'clock there was not a man, or a boy over twelve years old, left on the farms. All had gone up the dark New Road toward the mountain, on carts loaded with shovels, axes, buckets, and lanterns. Only children, unknowing, slept soundly. The women napped, and waited for the dawn.

Oh, for rain! For rain! Or, at the very least, a windless day.

But the sun came up hot, a ruddy ball behind a screen of smoke, and a breeze came with it from the south. There was not a cloud in the sky. All day the women who had horses they could drive carried food cooked by other women and left it with Norman and Hasty women, who were nearest to the fire and who were frying doughnuts and keeping pails of coffee ready for fire-fighters who could come for it.

"I don't know how long they'll let me stay here," said Mrs. Norman grimly. "But I'll stay till I'm drove."

"They'll let you know," the other women told her. "They won't let you be cut off."

"Be cut off theirselves, don't look out. They're starting a backfire, since it jumped the brook."

"Maybe the wind will change."

"Pray for rain."

"God knows I'm praying, but I can't get words out for coughing from the smoke."

At dusk the wind went down and the dew fell; but what was dew to a fire that had now burned over two-thirds of the McIntire lot, the biggest timber in the

county, and was leaping from treetop to treetop? From
our place the whole eastern sky was curtained in red and
we could see the flames shoot up.

Nobody went to bed. Children drowsed fitfully in
chairs and women went from window to window, or
paced the yards.

"It's coming this way. You can tell it is. Normans'
may be gone by now. If it gets to the road, it will take
Clarence's. If it crosses the road it will take Charles's
and Uncle Gran's. Then what is to stop it from coming
down through the woods to Earles'? And from there
wind from the south again tomorrow will bring it right
through here. We don't have many horses. And what
is happening to the men in that inferno? Dear God, are
we all going to go?"

But about one o'clock that night there was a new
kind of fire in the sky. A lightning flash followed by a
long roll of thunder, then more and more of both in
quick succession, and suddenly the rain came down in
sheets, in torrents, in masses like the waves at the beach.
And before the first shower had passed, another came
up, with a downpour as heavy as the first. The red glow
shrank, narrowed, and disappeared behind the trees.

"Well, that's about it," said Vinnie. "The menfolks
will be home in a few hours. It'll take them that long to
figure out who to leave on watch, and to load up and get
here. When they come, they'll be dirty and hungry.
We'd better get a little sleep before then."

"Oh, how thankful," Frankie whispered, "how thankful I'll be when I see their faces. I'll lie down, but I
don't believe I can sleep."

She did not think she did, but quite suddenly Verd came into their chamber and she saw that there was light enough, without a lamp, for him to pour water into the bowl.

She sat up on the side of the bed.

"Verd! You're home! Fire all out?"

"Near enough." He was hoarse. "The Navy Yard sent up some Marines to watch it."

"Did it — did it burn any houses?"

"Didn't get within a mile of a house. Went straight through the McIntire lot, though."

"Oh." Frankie was putting on a wrapper over her nightgown. "Well, you must be starved for a hot meal. Come down as soon as you've washed, and I'll have it on the table. Then you can sleep the sleep of the just."

As she was going out of the door, Verd mumbled a few words through a soaped cloth.

Frankie stood still in the doorway and stared at him. *"What did you say?"*

"Said, 'Hal got here all right, I s'pose'?"

"Hal! Didn't he come with you?"

The cloth dropped. Verd stood there, stripped to the waist, black with soot, his throat raw from smoke, and stared bleakly back at her.

"I started him out of the woods three hours ago. Soon as it begun to rain. He was dog-tired, but I took him out to the New Road and started him this way, told him to keep going and before long he'd know where he was . . . He *must* have come. You been asleep?"

"No. Not more than half, anyway. I'd have heard him. I was *listening*. Oh, Verd!"

He reached dully for his shirt.

"Must have taken some wrong turn in that rain. It *was* pitch-dark . . . Oh, God! I've got to go back up into the woods — and don't seem as if I could take another step!"

George called from the foot of the stairs. "You say Hal didn't get here?"

Vinnie opened the parlor door and said, "I keep *telling* you — Hal's home! Came in before I went to sleep and washed at the sink. I went out and got his supper. He ate like a stevedore and has been abed and asleep for hours. For heaven's sake, you men clean up while Frankie and I get your breakfast. Father, you look like a chimney sweep."

"Worst fire I ever see," he told her. "Hadn't been for that rain would have swept the township."

"Hadn't been for Lula and Frankie being where they saw the start of it, and so many of you getting at it so fast, might have swept the township before the rain came. Nobody hurt?"

"No, as luck would have it. Three of 'em got sur-rounded, but we got 'em out with a chain passing buckets."

"Verd said it swept your McIntire lot."

"Did. But a good many other lots was hurt worse. Young growth. The trees on the McIntire lot was big enough to stand it."

"Have to sell it for sawing as soon as you can, though, won't you? Rot, won't it, if it stands long after fire's been through?"

"Ready for sawing, anyway. Growed all 't would."

"But the dealers will try to beat you down, knowing you can't hold off as you could have once."

"I can hold off till I get my price. And will."

Vinnie laughed.

"They'll be gathering here within a week, like bees around a hive, trying to make out they'd be doing you a great favor to buy at half that much."

"I'll be twenty or thirty feet below ground. Got a well to dig. Dealers had better talk sense or save their breath."

"They'd better. But they won't. Till they have to . . . There, sit down, both of you. We might as well have something, too, Frankie. You're pale as a ghost."

"With thankfulness," said Frankie. "I can't eat but I'll have my tea and just sit here and be thankful."

It was full daylight now, with the air washed clean, the sky full of scudding clouds, and the birds singing.

"I never remembered till this minute," said Frankie, "that the beach sand and shells I brought for Marcy are still in the back of Lula's wagon. We'll have to go up tonight, Verd, and get them for her . . . After you've had your sleep."

SEPTEMBER

SEPTEMBER is a banner of soft purple and metallic gold proudly suspended across the sky and reflecting not only its royal color upon the earth but its power upon people, as strong sunlight through curved glass lying in a dry place releases energy, ambition, determination, and sets it aflame.

The sandy roads are bordered deep in goldenrod and wild asters. Sweet apples and Porters are yellow in the orchards, and blue pearmains are ripening. Maple trees are touched with yellow from the first frost. Pumpkins are drawn by the cartload from the fields and stacked beside the barn. Every morning at dawn there is the sound of the saw and the axe in the dooryard, and every day the pile of split wood grows.

There is the smell of the dye in the new cloth being cut and stitched into new shirts and dresses to be worn to school, and in the new shoes which shine to be looked at and squeak to be heard. And the smell of the dye mingles with the smell of hot vinegar and spices for the dozen kinds of pickle being bottled and sealed for the winter.

The calves of the spring have become heifers and steers, losing their sleepy gentleness and acquiring confidence and grace. The chickens have lost their down and ceased to peep, are now half-grown, with feathers which mark both their sex and their breed, and have begun to learn their language, to practice tentative *cut-cut*'s and *cocka*'s which they cannot yet quite complete but know they will with time and effort, and so strut about the pen, feeling superior to old hens with crusty feet and bare spots on their backs, and to old roosters whose combs will never again be as brilliant as they once were. The future belongs to the young, and the young must claim and use it before they discover that the past, too, is treasure stored up in an impregnable vault.

The district schools open a week before the Academy, and this September, each morning of Marcy's first week of school, Hal walked with her down the lane and west along the main road past the Dorr gate, over White's Marsh bridge, through the woods beside the river and up Nason's hill. The first morning, he went on with her to the school yard and told the new teacher, whose name was Miss Watts, that this was his sister, Marcy Hasty, coming to school for the first time. Miss Watts smiled and took Marcy's hand and asked her if she would like to learn to read. Marcy said she could read already, but she would like to have some new books. Miss Watts promised to find some for her, and Marcy saw Bernice's brother Clyde and her cousin Mabel Hasty, who was a big girl; another big girl whom Marcy had never seen before but who said her name was Laura put her arm around Marcy and admired her flowered hair ribbons. After that day Marcy did not want Hal to go with her farther than the top of Nason's Hill. From there she could see the schoolhouse, and the flag waving at the top of the pole, and the scholars climbing on the fence or chasing one another or sitting on the ground playing stick-knife; and she liked to run toward them alone with her book bag thumping against one knee and her lunch-box against the other. But she did not want to go through the woods by the river alone; she liked to have Hal with her in dark places.

"But I can't be, after tomorrow," he told her on Thursday. "Monday I'll be in the village long before you even start to school. I have to be at the Academy at ten minutes of eight."

"Then walk behind me today," said Marcy. "I'll pretend you're not there."

But he was. She could hear his footsteps all the way through the dark woods.

Friday morning she stopped on the bridge, at the end of the sunshine, and told Hal, "You can go home now. You can put the new chain on your bicycle pedals."

"Don't you want me even to come behind you? Even halfway to the hill?"

"No. I have to go alone Monday, so I might as well go alone now."

She plunged sturdily into the shadows and never once looked back to see that he waited on the bridge until she had gone out of sight. He came home and told his mother that Marcy would be all right now to go to school by herself.

He did not know that Marcy had taken him with her and would take him with her as long as she needed him for protection. She pretended that he *was* behind her, and heard his footsteps all the way, loud and clear.

It is easy, she found, to believe that something is there when it isn't; much easier than to believe that it isn't there when it is.

She always gave a skip as she came again into the sunshine at the top of the hill, and saw the little white building with the flag above it and her friends playing in the yard. It was a skip of joy in the prospect before her but also in her own power to bring people to her without their being aware of coming and to give herself company and security in the loneliest place she knew.

This September, Marcy began her first year of school and was Miss Watt's youngest scholar. She soon learned to leave her play the instant the bell began to ring and take her place at the head of the girls' line forming before the girls' door. When the bell stopped ringing, Miss Watts on the step and the two lines of scholars in the yard saluted the flag and repeated the pledge of allegiance. Then Marcy led the way into the girls' entry, where coats and caps were hung on pegs and rubbers left in a neat row along the wall, and passed to stand beside her small desk at the front of the room while the others marched to their places. Each morning they sang "America" before Miss Watts directed them to be seated and repeat the Lord's Prayer. After that, Teacher read from the Scriptures, and then said, "Take out the book you will use for your first recitation."

The schedule for the recitations of the day was written in Miss Watts's clear round hand on the blackboard beside the clock, and never varied.

Marcy sat front center, before Miss Watts's desk, between the corner which had the dark red papier-mâché water pail on a shelf and a blue enamel cup hanging by its handle from a nail and the corner where the bookcase stood with the globe on its green box beside it. All the walls between the windows were covered with blackboards and in September all the windows and both doors were wide open, letting in the smell of ripening fruit, wet pine and balsam, river water, and marsh hay drying on stilts.

Because words were old friends to Marcy she was in the third reading class, the second spelling class, and the primer history and geography classes. But because she could only write the figures up to 100 and did not know what else to do with them, she was the beginning arithmetic class all by herself, trying to catch up with Albra who, also alone, was adding, subtracting, and reciting the tables of two and three.

"I can add," she told Albra at the end of the first week. "Soon as I know take away, Teacher says I can begin to learn the tables just like you. So then I can be in your class."

"Ho!" laughed Albra, whose hair was red like the hair of Arthur who had kissed her on the Fourth of July and made a grass ring for her finger. "Don't

you s'pose by the time you start learning the two's I'll
be all the way up through the twelve's? You think
I'm likely to *wait?*''

She saw that to catch up with Albra she would have
to learn faster than Albra. Much faster than Albra,
because he was already so far ahead.

No one at school was waiting for anyone else. Marcy
sat in her small seat and heard the big boys and girls
reading and answering questions about *Silas Marner* and
The Vicar of Wakefield and *The Merchant of Venice.*
She heard them spell *pneumonia, embarrass, distinguish,
tintinnabulation* and give the definitions. She saw them
do arithmetic problems which covered a whole board, to
find out how long it would take and how much it would
cost to shingle a house, a shed, and a barn with a silo
at the end. And she saw them tap the maps with Miss
Watts's long pointer to show where Omaha was, and
Santa Cruz, the Amazon, the Nile, Edinburgh, Fujiyama,
Hong Kong, and Petrograd. She heard Miss Watts read
aloud the best themes they had written on ''The Stamp
Act Congress,'' ''The Battle of Bunker Hill,'' ''The
Meeting of General Grant and General Lee'' . . .

It was clear to Marcy that she had a great deal to
learn in this school before she was ready for the next,
and she wondered why she had not come here sooner to
begin.

But each noon she left the other scholars, always a
little reluctantly, and went across the road into another
world where there were altogether different subjects
for study. Because Frankie did not feel that a little
girl should be in the company of other children all day

long, she had arranged for Marcy to take her lunchbox
to the Nasons' every day when the noon hour began and
to stay with Mark and Lizann Nason until fifteen minutes
before Miss Watts would ring the bell for the afternoon session.

Mark and Lizann Nason are very old. They have
great-grandchildren the age of Marcy, but none of them
live in this district and Mark and Lizann do not see them
or their parents or grandparents often. Mark and Lizann have lived alone for many years, are accustomed to
their way of life and condone no other.

A little girl expected to eat her lunch there finds a
newspaper spread on the wide, scrubbed pine boards of
the floor under a window and a low chair placed on it.
She sits down and Lizann tucks the end of a fringed
white tray cloth into her collar. The fringe tickles her
chin and neck a little as it goes down. The cloth is
narrow, and long enough to cover Marcy's lap all the
way to the hem of the full skirt which Lizann jerks
decently over the bent knees.

"There, child," says Lizann.

The child is now forgotten until after dinner.

Mark and Lizann sit opposite each other at the small
table with legs which turn out at the bottom like wooden
feet below the soft folds of the last linen Lizann spun
from flax which Mark grew. Their profiles are toward
Marcy, and she sees the pioneer strength in their chins,
cheekbones, noses, ears, and high temples. The skin of
their hands and faces is dry and wrinkled, but brown
and tough. Mark's hair is white and thick, curling over
his forehead, around his ears, and low in his neck.

Lizann's is dark and thin, combed sleekly up from her face and pinned into a knot on the top of her head. Mark is big and always wears a black shirt, a black tie, and black pants. Lizann is small and always wears a black dress with a white apron and a white collar. When they bow their heads for Mark to say grace, Marcy bows hers, too.

After the grace, Lizann pours their tea from the steaming pewter pot which looks to Marcy like a fat duck; pours it into blue cups without handles, set in deep saucers. She adds warm milk from a little pitcher with a pink house painted on the side — Marcy could draw a better house — and warm sugar from a bowl which is brown from the heat of the oven. It seems to be very important to keep the tea piping hot. But when she has passed Mark's cup and saucer to him, they turn tea into the saucers and set the cups aside on little glass plates like doll dishes. Then they begin to eat hungrily of their fish chowder, or soup with dumplings, or fish hash and johnnycake. From the grave, silent joy with which they eat, Marcy thinks it must taste very good. Not until they have finished the food do they lift first the saucers and then the cups to their lips. And not until they have drained their tea are they likely to speak.

"Them crabapples most ripe, be they?"

"Rip'nin', Lizann. Rip'nin'."

"Praise the Lord them trees come through the Big Freeze when the rest was killed. Make the best jelly ever I et."

"Master fine. Master fine, by the faith."

Mark takes a worn leather pouch from his pocket and slowly, lovingly, fills his pipe, pressing in the brown tobacco with his big thumb.

The funnel of the low cookstove goes through a hole in the fireboard into the chimney. On the shelf above it there are a tall purple glass lamp, a brass candlestick with a yellow candle half burned down, an open tin box with the pink ends of matches sticking out, and a brown glass bottle which holds kerosene. Behind the stove the woodbox is full of wood and kindling. From hooks on the frame of the fireboard hang long-handled forks and spoons, an iron toaster, a copper basin, and kettle covers. Bundles of fragrant herbs are suspended from the ceiling beams, drying. In the corner stands a churn. Between the windows is the dry sink where Lizann sets her dishpan. There is a bench along the opposite wall where her washtubs and boiler are turned upside down. Beyond that is her flour barrel with her cakeboard covering it and a white cloth covering the cakeboard. Here is all that Lizann needs to keep her house, and all in order.

"Hear Charles Bennett has got him a new horse," Mark says.

"That so? Seen the critter, have ye?"

"No. Thinks likely I'll walk over there 'fore milkin' time, and have me a look into Charles's barn."

Lizann rises and brings her dishpan to the sink.

"Take your tray cloth by the corners and car' it to the door and shake it," she told Marcy the first day. "Bring it back and fold it in the creases and lay it on the table . . . Now set back your chair and fold up the

paper and put it in the woodbox . . . There, after this
you'll know how to do 'thout my tellin' it over. Now
you can go out in the yard and walk about nice. Don't
race so quick after eatin'. I'll call out when it wants a
quarter of the hour.''

Marcy went through the door and saw the berries
turning purple on the woodbine which clung to its frame
and to the weather-beaten shingles of the wall. The
sudden sunshine was so bright it made her blink. Mark
followed her, sat down on the door rock and lit his pipe.
He may fill it in the house, but he never smokes it there.

''Our boy Frank,'' he told Marcy, touching a hollow
in the rock, ''musta wore this with the seat of his pants.
Set here every night after supper, year he was seven, and
read the Bible through to Lizann and me. Both testa-
ments, all the way through. Quite a reader, Frank was.''

Marcy walked beside the wall, running her fingers
across the gray shingles. They were different from the
painted clapboards of her house. They had creases up
and down.

She stopped by the open door of Mark's little barn
and saw the forefeet and big eyes of his oxen in their
stalls. She came back toward the house and tiptoed up
and down the slanting bulkhead several times; there
was no bulkhead at her house; there the vegetables were
carried into the cellar through the shed. She peered
into the rain barrel and saw the moss on its sides, the
daddy longlegs walking on the water. She stood under
the pear tree, looking up at the golden fruit hanging
heavy with sweetness, and wondered if one should drop
at her feet whether it would be hers. A flock of small

birds, with a great rustling of wings, lighted on the slender branches above her, making them tremble.

"Going south they be," Mark said; and to the birds, "Mind you keep clear of the line gales, now. I've seen winds, middle of this month, would pull out your putty feathers."

Here was wisdom, safety, completion, peace.

But, "Quarter to, child!" Lizann called from the window, and Marcy raced across the road and was swallowed up in intersecting circles of shouting, pushing boys and girls to whom the future belonged.

"Run like a jackrabbit," said Mark to himself.

But Lizann heard him.

"As if shot out of a gun," she said. "That's how 'tis with young ones. Allus in an all-fired hurry to git wherever they put out for. Ye can tell 'em slow and steady wins the race but ye're blowin' your breath against the wind and hed better kep' it to cool your porridge."

There is more to learn at school than is in the books. You have to keep your desk tidy or your papers will get wrinkled and when you reach for a book your apple will roll out and Teacher will put it in her desk drawer and you will not have it to eat at recess. Every afternoon at closing time a few scholars of varying heights have earned the privilege of erasing the blackboards and beating the erasers clean against the clapboards. Once a week boards and erasers are washed with soap and water, ink is made and the inkwells are washed and filled by the most diligent scholars. Only a trusted boy is sent to the shed for wood or to the spring with the pail.

Only a capable girl is allowed to light the fire in the stove on a chilly morning.

One day when she came home Marcy was wide-eyed.

She told her mother, "Dorothy Plaisted pinched me today."

"If she does it again," said Frankie, "pinch her back."

The next day Dorothy pinched Marcy, and Marcy pinched Dorothy.

"Oh!" squeaked Dorothy in astonishment. "You *mustn't* pinch *me!*"

"I have to," Marcy told her gravely. "I don't like to but I have to. My mother says so."

Hal was beginning his freshman year at the Academy, riding the five miles down and five miles back on his bicycle on fair days, riding with Verd on stormy mornings and walking home if the sky had cleared by afternoon or studying in the paint shop if it hadn't. His courses were in English, Latin, Algebra, Ancient History, and General Science. He was known as a student now, and his teachers addressed him as Mr. Hasty. But his fellow students, for the most part, had grown up in the village or a neighboring village, wore clothes of a different cut and finer material than his, were accustomed to sidewalks, electric light, water from faucets, the use of a library, Chautauqua programs, morality plays, and formal teas and dances.

Hal endured Haze Week with good grace. He shinnied up the greased pole in the boys' basement while upperclassmen stood below with pins to speed his climb. He obeyed the call to the edge of the swimming pool and allowed himself to be thrown in, fully dressed, though he was fortunate that Verd had an extra pair of paint-stained overalls and a frock at the shop for him to change into. These were several sizes too large and he came into the house, carrying his wet bundle, as if draped in spotted sheets.

"Such foolishness I never heard of," Frankie scolded. "Four-year-old boys that have never been to school at all should know better."

"It only lasts a week," Hal told her. "It's part of the Academy tradition for freshmen. They say it's nothing to the hazing in the colleges."

"In *college!*" cried Frankie. "When they're grown men? Is *that* how ones act out that are learning how to carry on the government and make the laws and doctor us and preach from great pulpits? Dear Lord, what is the world coming to?"

"I guess it's always been this way. I don't mind the things they *do*. It's what some of them *say*. They call me Hayseed Hasty and Hick Hasty and they ask me, 'Haow's yer pertaters dewin', Herald?' or 'Hev they got their bewts on up in the sticks terday?'"

"I went to high school in Dover," Frankie said. "Over there they call people from the villages hayseeds and hicks. Maybe in Boston they call people from Dover hayseeds and hicks. But I shouldn't think people who do that could claim to have made much use of the advantages they seem to think living all in a bunch has provided them with. They don't all do it, do they?"

"No. Most of them are polite. But it's kind of condescending."

"Maybe that's in your own mind. Being polite is enough to start with. The other kind is not worth noticing. Pretend you don't hear them. Or tell them your potatoes are doing fine and will pay for all your school supplies and clothes for the year. I doubt if many of them are covering their own expenses."

"Likely it was some of their folks got lost on the side of the mountain when I was a boy," said George. "Come dark I heard them screeching, 'Lo — ost! Lo — st!' up there *in the sticks*. I wa'n't but seven or eight years old, but I went up and led 'em out to their carriage. They was dressed like ladies and gentlemen. One of 'em give me a ten-cent piece. Ten cents for walking two miles up there and two miles home again! Folks at home said I should have throwed it at 'em, but I figured even a ten-cent piece was better to have than to throw."

"Sometimes I don't talk right, I guess," Hal said. "In the General Science class we had to fill some test tubes for an experiment. I was looking for something to pour through and they asked me what I was looking for and I said, 'A tunnel.' Everybody laughed, and the teacher said the right word was 'funnel'."

"We've always said 'tunnel' here," said Frankie. "I'll write and ask Vinnie."

Vinnie replied promptly:

"Tell Hal his dictionary is his best guide. Tell him to look up 'tunnel' and he will find that one of the definitions is 'funnel.' 'Tunnel' is the older word but it is not obsolete. It is correct as he used it. But now that men tunnel through mountains for railroad passage, 'funnel' is more commonly used for the cone-shaped utensil we pour through. Tell Hal that many of the words we use are old English and Scotch words many Americans have forgotten and many others have never known. But they are good words and he can be proud of them. They are part of his heritage.''

Here at home September was like all Septembers until the last week. There were light frosts against which the more delicate plants had to be covered with grain bags weighted down with small stones, and three days of heavy rain and gale winds when all windows and doors had to be closed and the woodpile was covered with rubber blankets. But most of the days were warm and bright, and the fall harvest had begun. Frankie was salting down tomatoes in crocks since her preserve jars were already filled; baking apple and squash pies; stringing apples to dry in long chains hung from clotheslines and protected from flies by cheesecloth; and grieving because there would be no more services in the church until next summer.

''Just as well,'' said George, lying on the kitchen couch after supper, watching her peel and quarter. ''The Elder's banked us up with enough of the Good Word to last us through to church time again; or ought to. And he'll have his hands full with his own church in bad traveling; that and seeing to the schools and earning his living.''

''I don't see why Tatnic folks can have services all winter and we can't.''

''Because they've got the Elder.''

''We ought to be able to get somebody else to preach,

at least once a month, when he can't. One of the village ministers, maybe.''

''No, you don't want anybody but the Elder. That's been tried before and you know it. It's too resky. Know why we and Tatnic folks and Knight's Pond folks all have separate churches now, don't you? Because when they all went to the same one, at the crossroads, they had a minister come there that told them babies that died without being baptized was damned. Old Mr. Emery rose up in his pew, took his wife by the hand, said, 'We're not staying to listen to that doctrine,' and walked out. A good many other ones felt the same way. But some didn't. That was before I was born . . . But it's happened again since, right in our own church, ministers and members that thought like the ministers trying to force their doctrine on other ones and driving them out. Don't forget I've been drove, by the talk that went on amongst the temperance signers because I took a swaller from the jug of a old drunkard that needed company when he was beside himself over the death of his little girl. Don't forget Vinnie was drove when a minister she fed and bedded down here Saturday night preached Sunday morning about the sin of putting up a calendar that advertised liquor even though the advertising was all covered up with ribbon and paper lace and nothing showed (onless you pulled up the paper lace) but the head of a young one holding a kitten against her cheek.''

''I know there's been trouble,'' said Frankie stubbornly, ''but I don't think that's reason for not having church services or not going to church.''

Verd, knowing his father's views and how Frankie had been brought up, that his father's religion was a matter of logic and Frankie's of emotions, folded his newspaper, lighted his hand lamp, and asked Marcy if she wasn't ready for bed. It seemed to him risky even to talk about churches and what went on in them.

But Marcy shook her head. She tried to imagine the Elder lifting the paper lace on a bedroom calendar to see what was printed under it, and could not; so she knew it was wrong, even somehow shameful. To say nothing of talking about it in public!

"That's because you've never been mixed up in it, Frank," said George calmly. "Since you was old enough to think about what was said and done in church, it's been the Elder's church, and such things don't happen there. Anybody who believes in God and seeks him can go to a church where the Elder preaches and find Him — *onless* he believes that God can only be found where *everybody believes the same way.* I've always thought God give every one of us a mind to use, and every one of 'em different, and expects us to use 'em, not be led around by the nose by ministers or church members or anyone else. The apostle Paul said 'whosoever shall call upon the name of the Lord shall be saved.' Romans 10:13. But almost ever since there was a church to go to some in it have been bound that what they believed was what everybody else had to believe, and anybody that didn't was headed for hell. So the Catholics couldn't go to the Jewish tabernacles, and the Protestants couldn't go to the Catholic churches, and since then the Protestants have split up into so many sects you can't hardly count

'em. There's I don't know how many kinds of Lutherans,
and there's Quakers and Shakers, and Presbyterians, and
there's Episcopalians and Methodist Episcopalians, and
there's Baptists and Free Will Baptists and Christian
Baptists, and there's Congregationalists and Universal-
ists and Unitarians, and I don't know what all. You'd
think all this splitting up would have learnt everybody
what the Elder knows — that a church is a House of
God where God-fearing men and women ought to be able
to find Him according to their own lights; that a man's
religion, if he's got one, is a matter between him and God
and not to be tampered with — but it hain't. Soon as a
new church is built it gets a membership and a minister
and they start tampering. Makes you wonder if human
beings are ever going to get a decent respect for minds
that God created. Ontil they do, there won't be many
sermons to match the Elder's and folks that set before
him Sundays even three months out of the year are
mighty favored.''

Frankie was silent, beginning to string the apples she
had quartered.

''Well, Father,'' she said at last, ''I don't know but
you're right. Because, as 'tis, you and I can go to the
same church even though there's hardly a passage in the
Bible that means the same thing to both of us . . . But
if ever we don't have the Elder I'm going to start
looking for another like him. I can't do without a church
to go to, for years at a stretch, way you have sometimes.''

''I hope you can find you another one like the Elder,''
George told her. ''And if you do I hope I'll be alive and
have my eyesight so's't I can gaze on his face.''

The next day Marcy burst in from school in a state of considerable excitement.

"Mama! Mama, Teacher says for me to find out what day we're going to Rochester Fair!"

Frankie closed the oven door and took a few steps back from the heat, wiping her floury hands on her apron.

"What makes her think we're going to Rochester Fair?"

"She said probably everybody was, and we get a day off from school for it. Tomorrow we have to vote which day. Teacher says this is a democracy, so we'll get the day that the most of us vote for. The Fair runs from Monday to Friday, but nobody wants to go Monday because that's the first day and some of the exhibits won't be up then; and nobody wants to go Friday because some of the exhibits will be gone and the flowers in the Big Hall won't be fresh. Which day are we going?"

"Hang up your jacket," said Frankie. "And put your lunchbox in the sink." She sat down in the rocker by the back window and sighed. "We never go to the Fair. You know that. I never went myself until we lived in Rochester, and I've never been since."

"Teacher said probably *everybody* — "

"She doesn't know the Hastys yet. Nor the Brookses."

Frankie's mother was born Louise Brooks, and though she has been married twice she has been no man's wife as long as she has been the daughter of James and Catherine Brooks.

Marcy's lip began to tremble.

"Are we different?"

"About Fair-going anyway. The Brookses have always

thought Fair-going was sinful because men drink there, and there are games of chance, and they bet on horse races. Hastys think it is a waste of time, that a day spent there leaves too much work undone at home; besides, it costs money to get there, and money for admission, and the Fairground is a dusty, dirty place.''

"What do *you* think?"

Frankie told the truth.

She said, "I liked it when I went. The Hall of Flowers was the most beautiful place I was ever in, except the time I visited Bertha Harwood in Lynn and her mother took us to the Parker House for dinner and the whole ceiling was hung with chandeliers. There was another hall full of canned things that looked delicious and fancy work of all kinds and quilts with stitches so fine you could hardly see them. We went around to see the cows and steers and hens and they were big and handsome like the ones painted in pictures. And we watched the racing, and the horses were pretty and ran as if they loved it. I didn't see any harm in any of it. But I was thirty years old. I don't think it's any place for children, though I know many children are taken there.''

"Teacher said *everybody* — "

Marcy ran upstairs. Frankie did not follow her. Children must learn that there is very little in life which everybody does, right or wrong, wise or foolish.

The next afternoon each of Miss Watts's scholars wrote a choice of days on a slip of paper and dropped it through a slot in the cover of a shoebox. Three people by turns counted the ballots to be sure there were just as many as there were scholars at school that day. Then the ballots were divided and counted according to the days of the week. There were more votes for Tuesday than for any other day.

So the next Tuesday Marcy was at home. It did not matter, she thought, where she was since she was not at the Fair. She dawdled over the breakfast dishes. Frankie, at the ironing board, felt her accusing stare.

"For heaven's sake, put on your jacket, Marcy, and go out and play. It will be too cold soon enough."

Marcy went out and sat on the step. She did not play. Tomorrow all the other scholars would be telling of what they had seen at the Fair. Hastys never went anywhere. Hastys saw only the same old things, year in and year out. First it was spring and then it was summer and then it was fall and then it was winter again.

The Academy, too, was closed for the Fair that day. Hal was in the field above the barn, digging his potatoes. Verd and George were digging potatoes down by the pasture. This might be Fair time for everybody else. It was digging time for Hastys. Marcy wondered rebelliously why she had not been born into a family who went where exciting events were taking place.

Suddenly Verd appeared over the hill waving his hat.

"Hal! . . . Hal, hear that noise down over Rocky Hills?"

Marcy saw Hal straighten to listen.

"What think 'tis, Hal?" Verd shouted.

"By golly, I — I bet it's a flying machine," Hal shouted back. He began running toward the house. "Marcy! I think there's a flying machine coming over! Quick! Tell Mama to come out!"

Frankie was the last to reach the top of the hill. Even George was there before her. And still there was nothing to be seen in the clear sky save a few fluffy clouds. But the noise was growing louder.

"There she comes!" Hal sang out. "There she comes!"

He sang it as if he had thrown this object into the sky like a kite and had it on a string; as if it were his machine. And so, in a way, it was; his and Marcy's.

"I thought that's what it was," Verd told Frankie. "Some way, soon as I heard it, I thought that's what it was."

They saw it first as a dark speck, then as a big bird, with a raucous, buzzing voice, and then as a top buggy with two long wings instead of wheels. The noise it made now was almost deafening. It was not, actually, very high, and it was not moving very fast. It seemed almost to stop above the little group of Hastys on the hilltop in the field.

There was a man in it. Marcy could see his arm between the side of the buggy and the top. It had a white sleeve. She was jumping up and down and screaming, though nobody heard her because the voice of the machine drowned out hers.

But the man in the machine saw her. He saw her and waved the arm in the white sleeve. He even leaned a little to the side and smiled down at her.

"Look! He sees Marcy," cried Frankie. "He's smiling at her!"

"Don't! Don't!" screamed Marcy. "You'll tip over!"

But he only waved again, a big sweep of his arm, and

the flying machine went on, straight over the roof of the Hasty house, over the maple trees, over the river, and became a big bird, a dark speck, a noise dying away above the woods.

"Well, them as wants to ride that high is welcome to," said George, "for all of me."

He started down the hill to his digging in the earth he knew.

"I want to," Marcy said.

"Like enough some day you will," Hal told her. "Me too, I'll bet."

"Well, now I never thought," Verd said, "I'd ever see a man flying through the air over this hill."

They stood there, talking about it.

But Frankie had more ironing to do before it was time to cook dinner. She went back toward the house and Marcy went with her.

They said nothing on the way. At the door Frankie asked, "You coming in, or going to stay out?"

"I guess I'll stay out."

"Well, you've seen a flying machine."

"Yes."

"And the man in it waved to you."

"And smiled, and he never tipped over!"

"So you've had quite a day, after all, haven't you?"

"Yes . . . Oh, Mama, what if we hadn't been here? What if we'd been *off at the Fair?*"

OCTOBER

OCTOBER is age regal and triumphant, the impartial judge on the bench, the dowager duchess, wise, strong, and in excellent health, bearing easily the weight of velvet robes which change with shifting light from deep blue to plum color and crimson, of heavy chains, heavy pins, heavy rings all of gold, of the great keys of which this month is the keeper, of the coin of the realm secreted in the robe's capacious pockets. On the scroll held in these ringed hands is the summation, the business record of the farm year, and this no man can dispute. October cannot be gainsaid. That which it has in its pockets, in its cupboards and caves, is safe and held in trust to be distributed through the months ahead to those who earned it and so to whom it is due. What is not there will never be there.

There are heavy frosts at night, and though most of the days are bright and warm, some of them hot, the light perfumes of summer are gone and the smell of blackened vines sweeps in from the planted pieces

mingled only with that of burning potato tops. The
cornstalks stand in stacks like wigwams, ready to be
brought to the barns for use as bedding for cattle and
horses. Nothing remains in the fields but the cornstalks,
the cabbages, parsnips which will be left there until
spring, and wandering, wondering cows. Stoves have
been set up in chambers and sitting rooms. Men drive
to woodlots lately stripped and haul home cartloads of
sawdust for banking houses. Woodpiles in the yards are
growing smaller and the sheds are filling up as wheelbarrows trundle between, loaded high going in, empty
coming out. Chimney soot has been swept down. Women
are cutting patchwork to make new comforters and mend
old ones. The barn lofts are full of hay, the long, deep
chests of whole corn, cracked corn, and oats, each in its
compartment, the cellar of potatoes, squashes, pumpkins,
apples, carrots, beets, and other fruits and vegetables
in jars, pickles in crocks; or as full as they will ever be.
Herbs and popping corn swing from the rafters in the
shed chamber. The children gathered hickory and hazel
nuts after the first hard frost opened their burrs, and
these hang in baskets among the corn and herbs. The life
of the year has moved inside the buildings and seems to
swell their sides.

This October, George's sister came from Lawrence,
Massachusetts, to visit and stayed a week with him,
another week with their brother Granville. Her name
is Joanna as her mother's was, but she has always been
called Annie. She has celebrated her seventy-fifth birthday; her important birthdays are always celebrated;
before her seventieth she wrote all her Maine relatives,

"I'm not seventy years old. I'm seventy years young. Come up and see. There will be a party," and most of them went, even George. We have a photograph of her, all in white, taken that day when she was surrounded by Hasty women of all ages also in white or in white shirtwaists and black skirts and by Hasty men in black suits, boiled shirts, wing collars, bow ties, mustaches and muttonchop whiskers; also by Hamilton, Foster, and Harriman men, women, and children, for Annie has been married three times. On her seventieth birthday she had been the widow first of her cousin Lawrence Hamilton and then of a Mr. Frank Foster. Her third husband, Mr. Henry Harriman, was seated beside her for the picture, and he had a Vandyke beard. Now Annie is a widow again, but we Hastys have considered her a widow since Lawrence died, for it was he who took her from the house of her father, Joseph, to live in Lawrence on Hamilton Place. We knew him as one of our own and loved him; Vinnie lived with her Aunt Annie and Uncle Lawrence for a year when she was seven years old, because they had no children, while George and Sarah Jane had two others. To us Mr. Frank Foster was a kind friend of Annie's who provided for her generously, and Mr. Henry Harriman was another kind friend who later asked her to live in his beautiful home on Harriman Avenue. This kindness and generosity did not surprise us. Annie has always been beautiful, merry, confident, adored, and waited on hand and foot by her adorers; she still is all these. We have never known how we came by this entrancing creature.

At past seventy-five, with silver curls bouncing, gold

ear-baubles dancing, dark eyes a-sparkle, in a little white crocheted shawl (it had a gold thread in it), she pulled up her full, plum-colored silk skirt to free her small feet in their handmade kid boots with scalloped tops and jet buttons and played hide-and-seek with Marcy in the cornfield after school. Then she had to be taken to see the new litter of pigs and count them, to feed grain to the cows and let the horses take sugar from her hand.

"Do you walk the beams, Marcy?" she asked, looking up.

"Oh, no," Marcy answered virtuously. "I might get dizzy and fall and if I fell as far as that it might kill me. I've seen boys do it but it's foolish."

"Bosh," said Aunt Annie. "I used to walk the highest beams in the barn up home. You don't fall if you don't expect to. It's fun. I'd love to do it again. I've half a mind —"

"Oh, don't," begged Marcy. "I'll get more sugar for you to feed Bell —"

"Who told you it's foolish to walk beams? Your grandfather?"

"Yes. And, well, everybody . . ."

"But it was your grandfather told *them*, I surmise. Poor George! He always thought fun was foolish. I'm glad I don't. And you'd better not, Marcy! Wouldn't you like to have a pony?"

"Oh, yes! . . . I rode one once —"

"Why don't you have one then?"

"They cost a lot. To buy. And then to feed."

"Nonsense. Your grandfather's got plenty of money. Have you ever asked him to get you a pony?"

Marcy shook her head.

Aunt Annie laughed. "Don't dare? Is that it?"

It wasn't that.

"Well, I do," said Aunt Annie. "What a time you'd have, riding over these fields! Riding to school! Riding up to Uncle Gran's! I'm going to make George get you a pony."

At supper she sat beside George. She had laid off the little shawl and there was a wide, real lace collar over the plum silk now, fastened at her throat with a cameo pin. Her cheeks were pink from the wind, and in the lamplight her eyes sparkled more than ever. Marcy thought she looked like a fairy godmother, but had a dazed and doubtful feeling that she might be a witch in disguise.

Annie told George he did not look a day over fifty, that he was a handsome man, that she would never forget the first time she saw him after he and Sarah Jane were married, and both of them in their wedding clothes. She told him he had been a good boy to his mother, the most thoughtful of her nine children. She said it was a wonderful thing how he had made such a success of his life, starting out with nothing but this piece of ground his father had given him, and she knew it had been done by hard work and sacrifice and sound judgment. No wonder he had always had customers for everything he raised. There were no vegetables like these in the city of Lawrence. These beets and turnips, these good Green Mountain potatoes, this cabbage now — she did dearly love a boiled dinner and this was the best one she had had since she was here last time. Of course it was partly the way Frankie cooked them, but it was the flavor there was *in* them, too; something about George's soil, the seed he used, the time he brought them in.

"We've got a good well," George said filling her glass and his from the pitcher between them. "I lowered it ten feet or more last summer. It'll never go dry again."

Annie drank deep, her eyes shining appreciatively over the rim of the glass.

"Best water in the world, George. Right out of the side of Old Agamenticus! Frankie's been telling me what you did, and Vinnie wrote me about it too. Ah, there never was anything you couldn't do if you set out to. And the courage you've had all along! Who but you would have dared borrow money to buy your first woodlots? But you were proved right every time, George! Now you own the best lumber in this part of the state and don't owe a cent to anybody, do you? My stars, you are a smart man!"

Then she leaned close to him, putting her small, ringed hand over his rough brown one. As she moved, the scent of her cologne drifted through the kitchen.

"You had to be hard to do what you've done, dear. Hard on yourself and hard on your little family. But it's done now. You don't have to keep on. Why don't you take a little pleasure? Why don't you come up and make me a visit? I'm rattling around alone in that big house. You've never been there except to one birthday party. Come back with me and stay a couple

[197]

of weeks. We'll go into Boston and have a real Highland
fling. Cousin Mary Hamilton would love to see you, and
Ada's daughter Florence, too. She married now, you
know, and has some nice little children. And Melissa's
Hazel is up there with her little Jack, doing real well in
the business world —''

"No," said George. "No, I'm a cat in a strange garret
up around Boston. I'd be like Eben Blaisdell when
Bertha finally got him to go up to see her in Lynn. He
got there in the forenoon and she had a fine dinner for
him, but as soon as he had et he said he had to be
starting home. She said, 'Why, Eben, I thought you'd
stay a week anyway.' But Eben said no, he had just
bethought him that he had left three fleeces of wool in
his woodshed chamber and he was afraid if left there
longer they would create a spontaneous combustion.
Eben was always a great one for big words; talked like
a lawyer. So home he come, and it didn't seem hardly
worth the carfare.''

"I didn't suppose you would," said Annie softly. He
had moved his hand when he began to speak but she
found it again. "I really didn't suppose you would,"
she repeated slowly, softly, her warm, bright, dark eyes
looking straight into his steel-blue ones. "If people wait
too long to play, little brother, they stop wanting to.
Your joy is work. But there are people who still love
to play, and some of them are small now and will never
be small again. One of them sits at your table. Couldn't
you find pleasure in making her happy? Why don't you
buy her a pony?''

The silence which followed the sound of her tinkling

words was complete. Shock immobilized everyone in the room whose name was still Hasty.

"Buy — a *pony*," said George at last in a strange, muffled voice.

Annie's eyes shone like a cat's.

"Look at her, George. That little round eager face, shaped just like yours! Those two big eyes. Those braids tied in red ribbons. Can't you picture her bounding over your field on one of those shaggy little Shetland ponies that are all the rage now? Look at her!"

George looked at Marcy and she began to tremble. She saw his brown hand under Aunt Annie's little white one, his broad brown wrist below the blue flannel cuff of the shirt her Aunt Vinnie had made for him, his overall buckles on his chest, his smooth chin, his soft whiskers, and an expression on his face which she had never seen there before. There is a name for an expression like that but she did not know what it was. She only knew she could not bear it.

He cleared his throat. He was going to speak. What would he say?

Oh, Grandpa, don't . . .

"Well, no," said George, but still in that strange, muffled voice. "No, can't say as I can."

"No," Marcy burst out, as from a trap. "No I can't either, Grandpa. I'll bet — I'll bet ponies have fleas!"

She kept her gaze on him. She did not dare to look at Aunt Annie. Aunt Annie had meant well, but she — should have known better.

Annie only leaned back, threw up her pretty hands, and laughed until tears ran down her cheeks.

"Oh, George," she gasped. "What a lucky man you are! There's another chip off the old block!"

He pushed back his chair and led the way from the table. While Frankie was clearing away the dishes and Annie was asking Verd which stores he had painted the signs for in the village, George went into his room and sat on the side of the bed to change his steel-bottomed boots for carpet slippers. It was dark, for the days shorten in October, and he lit no lamp. But Marcy found him.

She climbed up beside him, feeling the cornhusks of his mattress with her knees, and pulled his head tight against her heart with all her strength.

"I love you, Grandpa," she whispered. "I *truly* love you."

He dropped the second boot and pushed his foot into the soft slipper. Then he freed his head and put his arm around her.

"You're a good young one," he told Marcy in his own firm voice. "Guess you and I, we'll make out, and have us suthin better'n a pony, to rights."

The leaves on the hardwood trees had been green, and George was stoning up his well when the first big car with nickel trim flashing white in the sunshine slid into the yard and the first lumber dealer, a tall, thin man in go-to-meeting clothes, set his brake, stepped out, looked around, and came to the door.

"Mr. Hasty at home?"

Frankie knew she had seen him before but did not remember his name, if she had ever heard it. She was wiping her hands on her apron.

"Yes. He's down in the well."

"In the well!"

Frankie laughed, remembering an often-told story of a very deliberate neighbor who had a little boy named Isaac and called Ikey. This neighbor had come into his kitchen one forenoon and begun hunting behind doors, under the sink, and on the top shelves of cupboards. Finally his wife asked, "What in tunket are you s'archin' after?" He answered slowly, patiently, "That ar rope. I want that ar rope," and went on looking where he had looked before. His wife wanted him out from under her feet, so after a while she said, "Well, tain't in here. Must be to the barn." He said no, he had hunted the barn over. "That ar rope must be in here some'eres." At last she asked in exasperation, "What have you got to have it for, anyway?" And he told her calmly, "Why, for Ikey, Mother. Ikey's in the well, you know; Ikey's in the well."

"He's dug it down," said Frankie. "Now he's stoning it up."

She went with the man to the edge of the well and Marcy went too.

Frankie called down, "Father! Somebody to see you!"

The man leaned over the edge, smiling broadly, and shouted, "Good morning! Good morning, Mr. Hasty!"

Morning? It was near noontime.

George bent back his head to glance up, said "How do," and studied the pile of stone on which he stood for one of the right size and shape.

Frankie went back to the house but Marcy stayed,

digging with an iron spoon into what had been a bank of mud dredged up from the well bottom and now was dry, except deep inside, with an outside crust like that on Indian bannock which Vinnie makes when she is at home.

"Fine morning, too," said the smiling stranger. "Don't feel as if fall is right around the corner, does it? I notice you're going to have plenty of winter apples, Mr. Hasty. Trees hang full out there."

"Them ain't winter apples," said George from below, fitting a stone to its brother.

"Ain't?"

"No."

"Thought they looked like Baldwins."

"Baldwins ain't that red this early. Them's Astrychans."

"That so? Well, Astrachans are good apples. I always say it's a sensible man that has a good orchard. An apple a day—"

George was climbing the ladder. He emerged from the well spattered with mud from head to foot, and in dripping rubber boots.

"You've got mud in your hair, Grandpa," said Marcy.

George reached the grass, picked up a straw hat he had left there — coarse straw and broad-rimmed — and covered his hair, mud and all.

"What you come about?" he demanded of the stranger. "That lot you've been hagglin' for and tryin' to beat me down on for two years?"

The stranger laughed.

"Thought I'd stop in as I was going by. Hear fire went through that growth."

"Did."

"Too bad."

"Didn't hurt it. Fire can't hurt trees as big as them."

"Trouble is, Mr. Hasty, anybody that buys it has got to cut it quick. Can't put off cutting lumber that fire has gone through. You know that as well as I do, Mr. Hasty. Man that buys that lot has got to put a mill onto it and saw like all get out, to get it while it's good."

"Nothin' to hender a man puttin' a mill onto it, fur as I know."

The stranger chuckled softly, archly.

"Got to buy it first, ain't he, Mr. Hasty? What's your price now?"

"Same as it's been. Twelve thousand."

The stranger whistled.

"Still saying that?" he asked incredulously.

"That's my price. And worth it."

"No," smiled the stranger. "No, nor never was, Mr. Hasty. Never was worth twelve. And now fire's been through it."

"Sartain fire's been through it. So ye think ye can get it for eight because I wun't dast hold out."

"Six, Mr. Hasty. Six thousand. Cash. That's my offer. Got a cashier's check right in my pocket."

"You offered eight a year ago."

"Before the fire . . . A fire's a fire, Mr. Hasty."

George looked out from under his hat at the stranger in his go-to-meeting clothes.

"Sartain," said George, evenly. "And a skunk's a skunk, Stacy. Guess my dinner's ready."

He went into the house. Marcy put down her iron spoon and followed him. The stranger stood there for a few minutes, lighting a cigar, and then got into his big gray car and rode away.

Scattered branches of maples had turned red and the woodbine berries were purple when a big black car with nickel trim flashing came into the yard and a fat man in a striped suit and a soft hat got out of it, looked around, and came to the door.

"Mr. Hasty at home?

"You'll find him in the shed there," said Frankie. "Just inside the door. He's sorting potatoes."

We have a bin for the potatoes to be used first, another for winter baking potatoes, another for potatoes to be boiled or used in chowders. The pigs' potatoes are kept in barrels in the cider cellar because that is where a great iron kettle was built into a brick stove at the base of the ell chimney for cooking or warming food for the stock.

Marcy was there, too, for it was late afternoon of a school day, and she was rolling little potatoes on the dirt floor, pretending they were marbles.

The stranger stood in the doorway, peering into the dim shed.

"Mr. Hasty? I'm Ray Wellington. You raise all these potatoes, did you? Look fine. You folks out here use a good many potatoes, I suppose."

George glanced up from where he sat on a stool, surrounded by potatoes and baskets.

"Buyin' lots, be ye?"

"Well, just browsing around a little today. We're pretty well supplied right now. Got any you want to sell?"

"Got one I would sell. Where ye from?"

"J. B. Neale Match in Portland. You may have done business with old J.B. He's dead now — dropped off some years ago. What's the lot you want to sell?"

"Didn't say want to. Said would."

"Not one of them in York that that bad fire went through?"

"Yup."

Ray Wellington drew in his breath through his teeth. "Hard luck!"

"Never believed in luck. Them as do might say it was my good luck my timber was big enough to stand it. 'Twan't hurt a mite."

"Still — well, some of it might saw out. How much do you figure it's got on it?"

"Prob'ly a million and a half."

"You do? Must have been quite a lot."

" 'Tis. Best lot in the county."

"What you asking for it?"

"Twelve."

"*Now?*"

"Now."

"Maybe I ought to look at it."

"Maybe you had."

"Can you show it?"

"I'll show you the boundaries if you want to buy it. You can see it from Hedgehog Rocks on the mountain road. All around it was small stuff, burnt to cinder. Chore time now.''

Ray Wellington came again two days later. Again it was late in the afternoon. George and Marcy were at the woodpile with two wheelbarrows. She could load one while he wheeled the other into the shed, stacked the wood, and brought the wheelbarrow back.

''Well, I went to York by way of the mountain road the other day. 'Most took the bottom out of my car, too. Couldn't see much, it was so near dark, so I came back yesterday and got a feller up the road to go round that lot of yours with me. You don't really think there's a million feet on it, do you?''

''Million and a half, or close to it.''

''Oh, come now. Don't believe they ever elect you town assessor, do they?''

George went to the shed and Ray Wellington followed him after a minute, but he did not go inside.

'' 'Bout all pine too,'' said George to the wheelbarrow as he came out.

''All *pine! That* lot! Hemlock scattered all through, and two-three acres of swamp spruce.''

''Hain't enough hemlock to kill Socrates. Keep out of the swamp. Close to a million and a half pine on the high ground. Lot of it'll saw into boards two feet wide.''

They were back at the woodpile. Ray Wellington put his foot on the chopping block but he was so fat it would not stay there. He grinned and sat down on the chopping block.

''Well, what do you want for it, spruce, hemlock, soot and all?''

"What ye offerin'?"

"Now give me your price and I'll come as near to it as I can. Get down to rock bottom because we're pretty well supplied. And, as I said, it's got a good deal of spruce and hemlock —"

George was on his way to the shed. Ray Wellington sighed and followed him.

"I've got to be getting back to Portland," he said in a loud voice.

"Go ahead," George shouted, stacking wood. "What's henderin' of ye?"

"Want to get this settled. Over and done with. Spent too much time and shoe leather on it now. What's your price for that lot?"

"What ye offerin'?"

"Well!" Ray Wellington sounded at the end of his patience. George came to the shed door and stood looking at him. "Well, have it your way. It's better than you could do anywhere else, but we're a pretty big concern. I guess we could give you five thousand for it. Cash on the line."

"Got to get my horse in," said George.

He disappeared into the barn. Old Bell was out to pasture. Marcy heard the whish of tin against oats, and the rumble of the tie-up door.

Ray Wellington went toward his car, came slowly back to the porch as if to leave a message, hesitated, pulled a big leaf off the woodbine and rolled it thoughtfully between his fingers. He dropped it on the step and it lay there like an old green worm sunning itself. He pushed it back and forth with the shiny russet toe of his shoe until it slipped through a crack. Then he went to the barn door.

Old Bell had come up the steep grade drawing her hindquarter haltingly after her but whinnying with eagerness and arching her neck.

"Oh, there you are, Mr. Hasty. Dark in here. But I guess you know this barn so well you could go all over it blindfolded without running into anything. Same with that lot of yours, maybe. You may be nearer right than I thought. Tell you what I'll do. I'll raise myself a full thousand. Call it six thousand dollars. How's that?"

"Double it."

Ray Wellington took a step or two backward, and began buttoning his coat. He assumed an odd position, with his weight on one foot, and screwed up his face. Marcy thought it was like someone in a school play, but there was no one there to see it except her and he had never noticed her at all. She thought perhaps he was practising.

"Oh, that's the idea you have, is it?" he said to the empty yard. "Well, well, if you get around to listen to reason, drop me a card, and maybe we can get together."

He climbed into his big black car and went away.

Annie had made her visit, and the road was bordered in red and yellow all the way from the village, the day George came home from market to find the big gray car blocking his way to the barn. He pulled up on the rein and said, " 'Hoa."

The man in go-to-meeting clothes got out of his car and came to the side of the wagon. He rested one foot on the hub of the wheel and it did not slip off, because he was tall and thin.

Marcy watched them from the porch. She had been kept from school that day by a cold, but Frankie had rigged her up warm to play in a sunny corner of the porch, out of the wind.

"Hello, Mr. Hasty! How are you? Certainly look hale and hearty. Lady told me you were about due back from town. Said you take butter and eggs and vegetables to customers on Fridays. Bet you have good ones, too . . . Well, I won't hold you up, Mr. Hasty. Get right to the point. Had another look at that lot of yours. The McIntire lot they call it. How about selling it to me for what I offered you a few weeks ago?"

George shook his head.

The dealer laughed.

"Oh, you're a stickler, I can see, Mr. Hasty. Well, I'll admit the lot has its good points, even if fire has gone through it. Pretty easy to get at, for one thing. Then, too, there's a little more on it than I thought." He rubbed his finger over a seam in the steel rim of the wheel. He took out a white handkerchief and dusted his finger, his sleeve, and the crease of his pants. Then he looked at George, smiling, with his head on one side like a listening squirrel. "Well, sir, I'll take a chance. I may be out of my head, but I'll give you — eight thousand! There, sir, I've said it and I'll stand by it. Eight thousand dollars spot down!"

George shook his head.

The dealer lifted his eyebrows. Suddenly he came up

beside George and leaned toward him with one gloved hand on the back of the seat and the other on the corner of the dashboard.

"You're out of *your* mind, Mr. Hasty! Here you've got a lot a fire's been through, be rotting by next summer. Isn't cut this winter it will be a total loss. I'm not a big concern, but you're way out of the traffic lines of the big concerns. I'm offering you a big price and taking a mighty big risk. Here it is the end of October. Unless we come to terms, I won't be in here over these roads again. Eight thousand, take it or leave it. What do you say?"

"I say I'm going to the barn, and you'd better get out from between my wheels," said George. "Back *up*, Bell!"

Bell backed, he gave her a flick of his lash whip, and incensed by such unaccustomed treatment as well as eager for her dinner, she reared in the harness, pranced like a colt across the grass, past the car and through the open barn door. A minute later the door rumbled shut. There was a dull thud as it hit the casing.

The man in go-to-meeting clothes went slowly toward the well. He pumped a great deal of water into the trough which carried it to the tubs in the cowyard. He took the tin dipper off the nail, rinsed it with care, and drank from it deliberately, staring at the barn. Then he got into his car and went away.

That night it rained. The next morning it was still raining, and all the leaves had turned brown. Marcy's cold was better, but this was Saturday, so she was still at home, wishing it would stop raining so that she could go out, or that she had a new book to read. George was sitting on the edge of a wooden tub in the shedroom shelling corn when the big black car came into the yard.

"That man from Portland is back, Father," Frankie called from the kitchen.

George opened the door onto the porch and went on shelling corn.

Ray Wellington bounced up the steps, took off his hat to shake the rain from it, and looked in.

"Well, Mr. Hasty, here's the bad penny. I'm not going to beat around the bush. You're the sharpest farmer I ever dealt with. Most always we can fool 'em or scare 'em but you've certainly held the whip hand. I'm going to admit Neale's Match has been trying to get hold of that McIntire lot for two years, through Bill Stacy. He can't beat you down and neither can I. We want to get a mill in there before the snow flies. I'm here to offer you your price — twelve thousand without the land. Cashier's check in my pocket."

"Let's see it," said George.

He went to the door.

"Looks all right," he said finally.

"Ride down with me now to the lawyer's for transfer of the deed?"

"No," said George. "But after I eat my dinner I'll meet you at his office. 'Bout two o'clock."

"Fine, Mr. Hasty. Fine."

As Mr. Wellington was getting into the big black car, George said from the shedroom door, "I'm going to tell you something. I figgered what you was up to when Stacy come here yesterday. He hain't got any eight thousand dollars. Puts most of his money on his back and into these dratted cars. Figgered then what Neale's Match was up to, and I don't think much of it. Old J.B. would turn over in his grave. He was no tricker. Way you've car'ed on, you'd never bought a lot of mine, hadn't been for the fire. Them's good clean trees on the McIntire lot. Taper like taller candles . . . But they ought to be cut this winter, and Neale's Match money is as clean as any. So I'll meet ye at two o'clock."

He shut the shedroom door.

After dinner he changed his clothes, harnessed Bell, and drove into the village.

He was back a little after three and asked where Marcy was.

"She's in on the front stairs," said Frankie, "writing a book. She's read all hers so many times she's tired of them. Why?"

"Got something here to show her."

"Marcy! Your grandfather wants you! . . . Marcy! *Marcy!* Are you deaf? Your grandfather wants you!"

She came out blinking. The kitchen looked small and almost empty. There was a woman with dark hair and purple eyes looking up from her sewing by the back window. There was an old man with a gray mustache and muttonchop whiskers standing by the table. She looked from one to the other.

"You better see this check," said the old man. "May be some time before you see one this big again."

He spoke quietly but she knew he was excited.

"How much is it writ for?" he asked her, pointing.

Marcy wrinkled her forehead. She had still not caught up to Albra in arithmetic.

"Twelve . . . Twelve hundred — dollars?"

"Count the zeros again."

"Twelve hundred — thousand? No, twelve — thousand."

"So 'tis . . . So 'tis . . . Twenty years ago I paid a hundred and fifty for that McIntire lot. Knew it would come on fast. Bound to. Best lot there is in this county now. Boards two feet wide in hundreds of them trees."

"How you must have felt, Father," said Frankie, "seeing fire racing through the tops of them! I'll never forget that night Lula and I were coming home from the beach. We thought we smelled smoke, and a few minutes afterward —"

Marcy was on her way back to the front stairs, and her dazzling new discovery — that she could build a world, put in it a school which little girls never left, and fill it with friends who did whatever she thought they would do. For all this she needed only a notebook and a pencil.

The notebook lay on the third stair. It had been Hal's last year, but many pages of it were still blank and he had given it to her. She had crossed out his name on the reddish-brown cover, and inscribed "Marcy Hasty's Property" above the crossing out.

She curled her feet under her on the second stair and began to read what she had written on the first few blank pages.

PRETTY ADA

Chapter 1

Ada was ten years old and she went to a boarding school the school where she went had a Junior and senior school the top of the place was used for the senior and the lower for the junior Ada was in the Junior part. She was a very pretty girl. She had dark Brown silky hair dark Brown eyes and a pretty refined little face and at the time my story opens was dressed in a pale green Muslin and had pale green ribbons on her hair she was out on the playground with another girl of an intirely diffrent type her hair was of a red color her eyes of a greenish color a freckled face and a very large mouth *She* was dressed in a bright scarlet dress with a bow of yellow ribbon on her hair her hair was not tidy like Adas but was tumbled and hanging about her face Peggy dear said Ada why carnt you dress better and were a hat (Ada had on a pretty white hat with little pink for-get-me-nots on it) and take care of your complention Oh Adie I am to wild for that sort of thing said Peggy . . . I want to know if you will go to Pine Hurst with me you know this is half holiday and there is no call for you to sit studying a stupid book all day. Oh Peggy dear I suppose I will go but I like to study and get my lesson's said Ada . . . . . they came in sight of a little vilage which was surrounded by Pines and all the houses had some pines and it was called Pine Hurst it was a very pretty Vilage it had a post-Office and a jeweler's shop they went to the post-Office and Peggy said I have a Parcel Post here and I would like to know how much it would cost. Well Missy I should think it would cost about ten cents he said extending his hand Peggy paid the bill and taking Ada's arm drew her out Well well what a pair said the shop tender Meanwhile Ada and Peggy were going toward the jewelers shop what do you want here asked Ada in surprise Oh I have a little business in here said Peggy soon she was out again and handing Ada a little box saying do not open it until you get home it is for you

---

Chapter 2

When Ada opened her box she found that it had four parts to it and in one part was a watch in one a pin in another beads in another bracelet Oh are they not handsome said Ada under her breath she had on her pale green dress and ribbons and she pined on her watch with her pin put her beads around her neck and put her bracelet on her arm and the gold went good with the pale green and as she went downstairs aleyes were turned upon her One little girl danced up and said Oh Adie what pretty jewelery do you like it Constance indeed I do said Constance looking at the watch attentively why se said that Watch must have cost fifty dollars or more Ada started for she had no idea its worth have you finished your theme Constance asked Ada Oh yes have you finished yours Oh yes said Ada I finished mine last night. You did said Constance in surprise I only finished about half an hour ago why have you to girls finished your theme my but arent you smart said another girl coming up Oh I don't think we are very smart Edna said Ada we have had time enough Well I have not finished mine said Edna gloomily and I dont see much prospects of my finishing it either. Why, carn't you think of any things to write asked Constance no said Edna I dont like to write themes it tires me to do it and the Teachers say I carnt make grammer and I dont expect I can and I try too. then you must try harder dear said Ada gently. well I get so discouraged said Edna Oh dont get discouraged because you can do it if you try hard yes I know it but it takes so long that I get all out of Patience said Edna sighing well dont feel bad over it said Constance who could never bear to hear any one sigh for as she was a bright and happie girl herself she thought it was a dreadfull thing but Ada knew it could not be helped and said we will talk about something else

Marcy stared at the clean blue lines below the last word.

"What next?" she asked herself in ecstasy. "What will they talk about? Where is Peggy? What will Ada say to Peggy when she comes?"

She groped for her pencil, her chin cupped in her left hand and her little finger in her mouth.

Alone in his room George sat on the side of his bed and looked at his check from the J. B. Neale Match Company. After a while he pulled a chest from under the bed, found his bankbook in it, and laid the check inside. The bank was not open on Saturday afternoon. He would have to go to the village again on Monday.

He sighed. It was too bad Sarah Jane could not know what that hundred and fifty dollars had done in twenty years.

Trees like great tallow candles. More than a million feet — maybe nearer a million and a half — of clear pine.

"Hadn't been for the fire," he thought, "never'd let it go to that Wellington. Talk, talk, talk; and most of it lies. Sucking up lies out of their slippery tongues. Making them into a cud of lies. Chewing it, swallowing it, coughing it up, and chewing it again . . . Never in this world, hadn't been for the fire . . ."

NOVEMBER

NOVEMBER is a russet apple with a glint of gold in its rough brown skin, one dry leaf clinging to its black-ened stem, and a brisk, spicy flavor at its core. It is cider working in dark barrels, reddish-brown sawdust blanket-ing the sills, amber-eyed cows chewing all day in the stanchions. It is stately fowl on yard parade in brown and gray feathers and red combs, and many brown eggs in the barn cellar nests at night. It is gray crocks filled with barberry sauce and great cubes of translucent pumpkin, scarlet cranberries drying in the open chamber. A lamp or lantern held high in the dark dairy reveals a mosaic of jellies, preserves, shrubs, wines, bottled herbs, and yellow cream rising on shallow pans. House doors are weather-stripped to keep out the cold, and windows polished to admit the thin gray light.

The farm has entered its long sleep. Buildings have become storehouses, and sing of their treasure.

It is time now to prepare the winter's meat.

The Butcher can come only on a Saturday afternoon,

as he works five days and a half each week on the town road crew. Most of the farmers do their own butchering but George Hasty never has, nor asked Verd to help him. George is an expert at dressing out, and dresses out beef, pork, and veal for his neighbors, earning, he says, far more than he pays The Butcher.

Like the rest of us, Marcy knows the circle of birth, life, and death and that each life has its own purpose. She likes to hear mice scampering happily in the partitions, and if one gets into the pantry she laughs at the way it sits up to listen if there is no sound and vanishes if there is. She watches the sides of the cat, the hog, and the cow swell, and the setting hen on the nest, knows there will be kittens, pigs, calves, and little gray and yellow chickens, and when they come hovers over them, names them, feeds them, carries the small ones about in her pinafore. But as time passes they grow and change, and she sees them as other than they were, knowing the cats will catch the mice, the pigs will stock the pork barrel, the heifers will have calves of their own and the bulls be sold or eaten, the hens, until they are too old, will lay eggs and sit on them, all the turkeys and most of the roosters will go to market.

She does not like to see a cat catch a mouse, but when the mouse no longer moves it is the cat's meat, and meat is good. She sees the bull calves bargained for, sold, led up ramps into carts, and driven away; and when she has asked where they are going has been told, ''To be veal.'' She knows this is the normal purpose, the accepted use for all but a few bull calves. Veal is delicious.

Once, watching George as he sat on a stool in the shed

with a rubber blanket across his knees, dipping a head-
less turkey into a kettle of boiling water and stripping
off the feathers, she asked, "Do you cut off their heads,
Grandpa?"

"Yes."

There was a red stain on the chopping block and on
the axe now driven into it.

"Does it hurt?"

"They never know what hit 'em. It's that quick. Like
blowing out a light."

"Do they know you're going to do it? Are they
scared?"

"How'd a turkey know what I'm going to do? He's
pecking corn here. I grab his legs with one hand and
off comes his head with t'other. The rest get kind of
excited for a minute and flutter around. Then they come
right back to the corn. A turkey's always happy filling
his gizzard. And my turkeys' gizzards are always full."

"I think turkeys and roosters are the handsomest,"
said Marcy admiringly. "In their feathers and when they
come out of the oven, too, all brown and crackly and
bubbly and smelling of butter and sage."

But it is different with pigs when The Butcher comes.

Other years Frankie has taken Marcy and gone to
spend butchering day with her mother and Lula. But
this year, with Vinnie away, she had to be at home to
get dinner and told herself that Marcy should not
longer be protected from the knowledge that pain cannot always be prevented and is sometimes necessary.

On Saturday mornings The Butcher does not fill his
dinner pail before he leaves his old black house at the

edge of the woods to go to work on the road. Much of the year, when the village whistles blow on Saturday noons, he gets into his wagon and drives home to cook his meat, boil his potatoes, and bake his johnnycake. A hot meal is a treat for The Butcher even though he has to cook it himself. He has never married, and the house where he lives is the house where he was born nobody knows how many years ago. He is always alone. Even when he is with other people he seems to be alone. But in the butchering season he does not have to cook dinner on Saturdays. The women, by turns, do it for him, with special care as for a priest before a ceremonial sacrifice.

Frankie had Marcy help with the preparations. They fried dried-apple fritters and Marcy noticed that Frankie flavored the filling and the sauce with cider, which she had never seen her do before, though it was always used in mincemeat. They boiled eggs and Marcy shelled and sliced them into the creamed salt fish. They cooked and mashed turnip, and opened and heated a can of tomatoes. There were hot biscuits and baked potatoes and bowls of sweet pepper relish, stewed huckleberries, wild grape jelly, and sour milk cheese.

"I *like* to be here when Blackie comes," Marcy said. She had heard her father and grandfather call The Butcher Blackie. "I never was before. Does everybody get a dinner like this for him when he comes?"

"I suppose we all do the best we can," Frankie answered. She added, thinking aloud, "I don't know why, altogether. It's not just because he's a lone man. A

French woodchopper is a lone man down from Canada but he sings at his work and whistles in his shanty and we don't have any urge to feed him unless we hear he's sick and may be hungry. A tramp is a lone man but we give him whatever comes to hand and let him sit on the step to eat it. I guess the difference is that the chopper is a happy man; we know he will go home in the spring and maybe bring his wife with him next fall. Even the tramp has hope, or he wouldn't keep moving on. But The Butcher has nothing — nobody, no happiness (as we know it), no hopes; nothing but — his work. Yet he is one of us, born and brought up here, and will never leave here. We are all he has, and we don't know him. We pity him, but we are afraid of him. We need him, we send for him, and all we can give him is his dinner and a dollar.'' She came back to Marcy. ''You shouldn't call him Blackie. His name is Simms. Call him Mr. Simms.''

''But he is certainly black,'' thought Marcy when he came.

He hitched his thin old black horse to a fence post, threw a ragged dark blanket over him, and hung a feed bag over his nose.

''Putty chilly today,'' said George from the barn door. ''Callate dinner's ready. Might's well eat.''

Mr. Simms took off his black cap with the visor and his flapping black coat and threw them onto the wagon seat. In his black overalls and black shirt with ragged sleeves he followed George into the house.

''Hello, Edmond,'' said Frankie with a timid smile.

"I'm just dishing up. Soon's you menfolks have washed in the sinkroom, it'll be on the table. Get him some hot water from the tank, Father."

While George was washing, Mr. Simms came back into the kitchen.

"This is your place, Edmond," said Frankie. "Sit right down and help yourself. You must be hungry."

She and Marcy were already seated. Suddenly Marcy shivered. She wished her chair were closer to her mother's.

The Butcher is a small man with narrow shoulders, but wiry. He had rolled up his sleeves to wash, and his swarthy arms are as big as those of a man weighing two hundred pounds, and all bulging muscle. His thin face is darker than his arms and his long, thick, curly hair is ink-black. So are his heavy eyebrows. His eyes are small, deep-set, black, and burn like live coals but never meet the eyes of another.

He reached with his fork for a potato and then for a second, swiftly cut them into quarters and heaped them with the creamed codfish. As his right hand dipped, his left hand reached with the fork for the biscuits, one after another until he had three. As he speared he dipped turnip with the same spoon he had used for the fish and Frankie hastened to take spoons from the plates under the bowls and stick them suggestively into the relishes.

She gave Marcy a potato and some of the fish, but neither of them wanted turnips with the cream sauce streaking it.

George did not mind. He took his place and helped

himself as usual, filled his glass with water. "There's cider in that pitcher by you, Blackie," he said, and bent over his plate.

The Butcher poured, drained the glass, and poured again. His plate was empty and he refilled it with the same swift sure motions of both hands.

"He must have learned how," thought Marcy, "by rubbing his stomach and patting his head." She had tried this many times, but never been able to do it.

Frankie said, "According to the almanac, it's going to be a long hard winter." No one spoke and she added, "Signs in the woods look like it, too; didn't you say, Father?"

George nodded. He had more than winter on his mind today. He would take the winter when it came.

"I'll cut the pie," said Frankie.

She had made a big mock-cherry pie of apple and cranberries and raisins. It was warm on the shelf of the stove and she cut it in quarters.

"Put mine right on my plate here," George said. "No need to dirt up extra dishes. Mine's as clean now as if it had been washed, 'bout."

So was The Butcher's. And in a minute or two both were as clean as before.

"Well, if you're through, Blackie," George said, "we'll turn 'em into the watering yard."

The men went out and Frankie began picking up the dishes.

"You didn't eat much, Marcy. Don't you want a little piece of pie?"

"No. I was watching — Mr. Simms. Can't he talk?"

"I don't know. I suppose so. I guess he speaks when he has to. He ate well enough, didn't he?"

"You didn't. You didn't eat anythng. Just drank your tea. Part of it. You weren't watching — Mr. Simms either."

"It's not polite to stare. Try not to do it."

"I didn't want to forget how he looks."

"I — wish I could."

"Why? Don't you like — Mr. Simms?"

"I don't like him or not like him. I'm sorry for him. But that doesn't do either of us any good . . . Marcy, put on your sweater and take this basket of chips. I'll take some wood and we'll build a fire in the chamber stove and you can play up there."

"Why? Are you going to work up there?"

"Yes . . . I have to tidy the bureau drawers."

As the fire crackled in the little box stove, Marcy knelt beside it, trying earnestly to make her left hand pat while her right hand rubbed.

"I don't see why I can't do this," she said. "Lots of them at school can."

"They start with their left hand," said Frankie. "Once the left hand is started it can keep going and the right hand can do something different. But whatever you start with your right hand the left will try to do the same."

"You mean my right hand is smarter?"

"You might say it's like some people, has more character, can do what it wants to or thinks it ought to do even if nobody else is doing it, has ideas of its own, doesn't have to tag after the rest —"

"What's that, Mama?"

"What's what?"

"That noise . . . That squealing noise."

"It's the hogs."

"Why are they squealing like that? Where are they?"

"They are in the watering yard." Frankie added quietly, "They are being killed. That has to happen before we have their meat to eat, you know."

"It hurts them?"

"Yes. For a little while."

"Grandpa says it doesn't hurt the turkeys and the roosters."

"No. But it's different with pigs."

"Is — Grandpa doing it?"

"No. Mr. Simms is doing it."

"Oh. That's why. Why — Mr. Simms is different from us."

"I shouldn't wonder if every time anybody hurts anybody else — even when he has to — it makes him a little different. And Mr. Simms has had to do it many, many times. It is his work."

"Why does he do that kind of work?"

"I don't know. But somebody has to."

The sounds were growing fainter.

"Can we see them?"

"I don't want to. I shouldn't think you'd want to. You would have to go into Hal's room."

Marcy thought about it. The sounds were so soft now that she could hardly hear them.

She said, "I want to, Mama. I want to see — everything there is."

She opened the door and went along through the cold upper hall into Hal's room and looked out of his window. The ground of the watering yard by the barn was strewn with red. The Butcher sat on the edge of the trough, smoking a pipe. One hog lay still, a great mound of white. The other was taking slow steps, weaving from side to side, but making no sound at all now that Marcy could hear. Suddenly he slid forward and became a second mound of white.

George came out of the barn and lifted one end of the first, and The Butcher, still smoking, lifted the other. They carried it into the shed. All the time they were gone the second mound did not move, and then they came back for it.

Marcy went into the warm chamber and put her arm around Frankie.

"You needn't feel bad any more, Mama," she said. "They don't hurt any more. They're pork now, I think. And it's starting to snow. If you don't look out for a little while you won't see the red in the watering yard, because the snow will cover it up."

She knelt again by the stove and considered which was her right hand. To decide, it was necessary to imagine herself coming down the church aisle and giving her hand to Elder Knight when she reached him. After a minute she began rubbing her stomach with her left hand and then found that she could pat her head with her right.

"I can do it, Mama," she cried. "Look! Look! It's just like you said! I can do it!"

"Oh, Marcy!" Frankie laughed with tears in her

eyes. "What would I ever do without you? Come, let's go down and wash the dinner dishes."

By supper time George had the hogs dressed out and hanging from the center beam in the shed.

"Good three hundred pounds of solid meat," he said.

During the next few days he cut it up. Smoke rose from the chimney of the little smokehouse back of the carriage shed where Verd was curing the ham and bacon. There was a fire all day in the stove in the shedroom where Frankie was trying out the fat to make lard. George packed great wedges of white meat into tubs of brine. Frankie pickled the feet and made hogshead cheese. The house was rich with the smell of frying and pickle and sage. Frankie cooked liver for supper and Verd would not taste it, so Marcy wouldn't, but George and Frankie liked it.

Finally the day came when Marcy proudly told the other children on the way home from school, "We're going to have fresh meat tonight."

Some of them said they had been having it for a week or more. Others looked at her in envy, saying that they did not know when The Butcher was coming to their house and that they did dearly love fresh meat, or even that all their pigs had died of a sickness in the summer and their mothers had to use lard in the beanpot. But one of these who had no pork at home said he had better than pork.

"My father shot a deer last week. We're letting it season but we'll have deer meat for Thanksgiving, and that's the best kind of fresh meat there is."

"Nobody at my house ever shot a deer," said Marcy. She was not sure whether to feel proud of that or ashamed. "I never saw one except in pictures. They're so pretty I don't see how anybody could bear to shoot one."

"Hoh, they kill hogs at your house, don't they?"

"Hogs aren't pretty. Besides, Mr. Simms does that."

"My father does it himself. I've watched him."

"Bet you never."

"I did so. My father says he don't waste money on The Butcher. Says a man can't afford to be too tender-hearted when he's got a family to feed. Anyway, nothing lives forever. Better for a deer to be shot in November, my father says, than to be run down by dogs in the deep snow. He shoots one 'most every year."

"My brother shoots rabbits and squirrels," Marcy said, thoughtfully. "Mama fricassees them. They're good. Papa cured some squirrel skins for Mama to make a collar for my best coat."

"Besides, if a hog lives too long he gets so big he can't walk. And if nobody shot any deer there'd be so many they'd eat up all our garden stuff; the same with rabbits."

"There's so many squirrels now it's hard to find nuts before they do. Nuts are strengthening when you don't have meat."

"And what if nobody caught any fish? Fish are pretty."

"I don't think so."

"Course they are. Snakes, too. And eels. Even angle-worms."

"Ugh! Nothing's pretty without fur or feathers."

"That's so. Guess that's why girls are so homely."

All the boys laughed, and the girls stuck out their tongues. Among them they had conquered squeamishness, quieted uneasy consciences, passed on to aesthetics, and were looking forward to their suppers with or without meat.

Near the middle of the month Marcy was wakened early one Saturday morning by excited voices and the clatter of dishes in the kitchen at the foot of the stairs.

"I think we ought to go right now, Papa," Hal was saying urgently. "What's to prevent somebody else from claiming him?"

"Now don't be foolish," Frankie said. "Nobody around here would do such a thing as that! Why, look at the years there's been a boat and nets under the bridge at York for catching alewives. Everybody uses them and takes care of them; nobody claims them. You've been long enough without something warm in your stomach."

"What time did you start out? What side of the pond was he on? How near you was he?" Verd sounded more excited than Hal did.

"He come down just after daybreak," said George. "I was building the fire and, s'I, 'Ain't you up early?' and s'e, 'I'm going to get my deer before breakfast, Grandpa'."

"Did he?" cried Frankie. "Did you really say that, Hal? Hold your plates. Here come the fritters."

Marcy was out of bed, putting on her slippers, scampering down the stairs.

The others were all at the table now, and all looking at Hal, all eating hungrily without seeing what they ate. It was Hal's hour.

"Well, see, I figured it all out last Sunday. I knew I could do it, but I didn't tell anybody because I wanted it to be a surprise. Of course I didn't know I'd get a buck —"

"Did you get a *buck*, Hal?" Marcy asked softly. "A *buck?* Honest?"

"Six points on his antlers," Hal told her with a sharp twist of his head, grinning with one eye half closed. "Well, see, walking over around the pond last Sunday I saw hoofmarks at the upper end where deer had come to drink, and halfway up the back side of the pond there's that old sawdust pile. So I dug me out a nice little blind near the top of the pile where I could lie and rest my gun on the peak and look over. I made up my mind I'd go over there early this morning and stretch out and watch and just wait until the deer came down. By the hoofmarks I thought there might be three or four come together. But I hadn't been there ten minutes when this buck came out of the woods alone. The sun was just rising over the mountain. It was right behind me, and shone on that buck so clear I could count the ripples on his legs. He was in no hurry, so neither was I. He drank and looked around and then drank again. When he had enough he threw up his head and looked all around again — and I fired, and he went down."

"One shot," Verd said. "Now that's the way to do it."

"Hal don't waste ammunition," George said approvingly. "How much d'you say he'll weigh?"

"A hundred and fifty, sure. More, I shouldn't wonder."

"Why, we'll have such a Thanksgiving dinner as we never had before," Frankie said. "I hope Vinnie can come home. I'll write to her. Maybe Hattie and George will bring her up."

"A hundred and fifty pounds," said Verd, "for the price of one bullet."

"Don't forget the price of his rifle," said George.

"Guess he's covered that too," said Verd.

"And don't think," Hal boasted, "this is the last one I'll ever get."

The men pushed back their chairs and Hal was one of them now, though only fourteen last April. They harnessed Bell into the cart, and Verd and Hal drove off over the lane toward the pond. When they came back they had the deer in the back and unloaded him beside the shed. Frankie put on her shawl and went out with her Brownie camera and took pictures of Hal crouching, gun across his knees, holding up the head to show the antlers with the six points. Then George began the dressing out. When that was done the deer was hung from a branch of one of the maple trees and all the rest of that day and the next men and boys were stopping by to see it and hear Hal tell the story of his first deer hunt.

"If you don't get one this year, Uncle Clarence," Hal said, "I'll give you a piece of the steak. You taught me to shoot."

"Tell Grace she can have a good piece for mincemeat," Frankie called out to Will.

Marcy heard the story so many times that it seemed to her she had been lying there on the sawdust heap, with her gun resting on its peak, looking across the misty pond while the sun rose over the mountain behind her and swept the mist away so that when the antlered buck came out of the woods toward the water she could see the ripples on his silky fur. She felt the cold damp of the sawdust at her elbows, her stomach, and her legs, and the faint warmth of the sun on the back of her neck. She smelled the November morning smells of frost-blackened ferns and rotting leaves and brown pine spills, listened to the stillness, saw the motionlessness of the November woods. Then out of it came this great brown creature on his long slender legs, this majestic creature with antlers flashing in the sun which shone on his rippling skin. She and he were alone, and he did not know she was there. He stopped at the edge of the water, lowered his head, and drank. She watched him. He lifted his head and looked all around but did not see her hidden by the sawdust. He drank again. In the stillness she could hear him drinking, as a horse drinks. He raised his head again, and she pulled the trigger because she was supposed to pull the trigger . . . And, next thing she knew, the Hastys were getting ready for such a Thanksgiving dinner as they never had before.

Actually, it was like all the Thanksgivings Marcy remembered — and will remember as long as she lives — with venison added.

On Tuesday when she came from school an iron kettle bubbled on the stove and the smell of spice, meat, fruit and hot cider filled the kitchen. Frankie dipped a

big spoonful into a saucer and handed Marcy a teaspoon.
"Taste the mincemeat," she said. "What else does it need?"

Marcy tasted and tasted again, could not think of anything in the world which might improve it, and scraped the saucer.

But Frankie tasted and added some brown sugar, a lump of butter, another handful of raisins.

"Now taste it," she told Marcy, dipping another spoonful into the saucer.

It was better than ever.

"Hal said there wasn't enough apple in it, and he was right. I put in four more."

"Maybe a little more nutmeg," said Marcy, not to be outdone.

Frankie rubbed the brown kernel briskly over the grater, tasted and said, "That *is* better."

But when Verd came in, she said, "Taste the mincemeat. I hope it's not too sweet for you, or too spiced up. I know you don't like it high-flavored."

He said it was prime.

That night the kettle cooled on the shedroom stove.

The next morning there were fires built in both stoves, to have two ovens to bake in, one slow for the Indian pudding, the other quicker for pies and cake. When Marcy came home from school that day the pudding was cooling on the sinkroom shelf, in the cellarway the racks were filled with pies, mince, pumpkin, and dried-apple; Frankie was just taking out the last loaf of applesauce cake. Before we went to bed we had polished the coin silver spoons and the steel blades and tines of the bone-handled knives and forks. Frankie had stood on a chair to reach the upper shelves of the sitting-room cupboard and passed to Verd the glass and china she used only on great occasions — Sarah Jane's amber goblets and square sauce dishes, and Frankie's own wedding plates and cups and saucers which have delicate green vines and leaves all around them and scalloped gold edges. Hal and Frankie had washed them all, while Verd polished apples — Strawberry Baldwins, Porters, and Northern Spies — and George cracked hickory nuts from which Marcy picked out the meat with a darning needle. Finally Frankie had made a thin maple frosting for the loaves of applesauce cake and, while Marcy sprinkled them with her nutmeats, had gone back to the sitting-room cupboard for a great glass compote on a high foot which had pictures of a deer in the woods on all four sides of it. Hal had washed this, and Verd had filled it with shining red apples and deep blue Concord grapes he had brought home that day from town in a covered, handled basket which he had given to Marcy to keep her doll's clothes in.

Still there was much to do on Thanksgiving morning. Frankie and Marcy had cleared away after breakfast and made the beds, the turkey had been roasting for a long time in the kitchen oven, and the venison had gone into the shedroom oven when George and Hattie and Roland and Vinnie rode into the yard at ten o'clock.

"Well, my sakes alive, doesn't take you long to get here in that, does it?"

"What time is it? . . . Well, there, we've been just under half an hour coming the whole fifteen miles."

"This is the buggy's last trip this year, though. Sunday we'll put it up on blocks in the shed and take off the tires."

"Vinnie, what have you done with Mr. Bannister?"

"Oh, his daughter Susie and her family came last night. I got everything started for her before I left. If she can't baste, and cook the vegetables and dish up — and I guess she can —"

"Hey, Hal, you old stick-in-the-mud, who set you up and never cropped your ears? Just because you shot a deer —"

"Marcy, *how* you *grow!*"

The men disappeared into the barn, and women filled the kitchen and shedroom. Frankie, in a gray bungalow apron covering most of her best garnet cashmere dress and wearing her engagement ring with its garnet stone surrounded by tiny pearls, produced from the bottom drawer of the bureau in the entry a bibbed apron in yellow to protect Vinnie's ruffled green silk and another in pink for Hattie who was wearing a pink batiste shirtwaist with a navy blue serge skirt. Somebody had dabbed perfume behind her ears, and it was probably Vinnie, for she wore earrings and her gold beads and her watch pinned among the green ruffles with a gold fleur-de-lis. Hattie wore no jewelry — she is always forgetting it — but her cheeks were pink as roses with the quick change from cold to heat; her smooth, heavy hair pinned in a coil on top of her head was like a copper crown slightly awry, and her hazel eyes danced with laughter. Hattie loves to come home, where to everyone who knew her when she went away she will never be more than sixteen.

"I brought some celery, Frankie," she said. "And here's the vase I put it in when George brought it when he came from the Yard last night. I'll just put in some water —"

"Oh, what a pretty vase, Hattie! Thin as an eggshell!"

It had festoons of tiny pink flowers all around it, and a gold edge.

"You like it? Somebody gave it to me. Plates like it, too, but they're all gone long ago. I don't like it, it breaks so easy. You can keep it."

"Oh, Hattie, I shouldn't!"

"You'll have to. I won't take it back with me. Probably break on the way."

"You going to use this tablecloth, Frank?"

"Oh, goodness no, Vinnie. I meant to have it changed before you got here —"

"I brought one I've just finished doing in cross-stitch. Why don't we christen it?"

She unfolded it and everyone exclaimed in admiration, for it was of brown linen with embroidered groups of stalking, red-wattled turkeys in the corners, and in the center there was a huge turkey on a silver platter, steaming hot (you could see the steam) in a heaped circle of fruit and nuts.

"Oh, Vinnie, what you can do with a needle!"

The familiar red cloth was whisked away, the table pulled out into the center of the room, leaves added to it, a quilted pad and the turkey cloth spread. The best glass and china came out of the sitting room. Marcy brought in the celery, and she and Vinnie began setting the table, while Frankie, between bastings, scrubbed potatoes and cut up squash in the shedroom, and Hattie, chewing sturdily on a match, peeled onions at the sink.

Open doors between the three rooms turned them into a banquet hall, and conversation ran freely from one end to the other. The men came in, cold, and stood warming themselves by the stoves as Frankie took out the turkey and set it back, covered with towels, to make room for Vinnie's biscuits in the oven.

"Smells all right," said Verd, modestly. "No saying how it will taste."

"Vinnie's biscuits," said her father, "are something I've been too long without lately."

"It's going to be the best dinner," cried Hattie, dipping sauces, jellies, relishes, "that ever we ate in our lives, any of us."

"I don't know," her father said. "One time when your mother and Vinnie was up visiting your Aunt Annie in Lawrence and you and I was keeping house, you cooked a pretty good dinner for Sam Watkins and me, and not much older than Marcy here either. You fried us a mess of pickerel I'd caught —"

"Oh, I was older than Marcy. I was eight. And I didn't salt them enough."

"So I said, 'Fish is a mite fresh, ain't it, Hattie?' And you had an answer for me. You said, 'Well, it's fresh fish, Father'."

They all laughed, none the less amused because they had all heard of this many times before. Hattie's cheeks flushed pinker. It was good to be with people who re-

membered what she had said and done when she was
eight.

Frankie opened the oven door of the shedroom stove
and a wonderful wild smell came out.

"Almost done," she said. "How are the biscuits coming, Vinnie?"

"Just beginning to brown."

"When will you be fifteen, Hal?" George Webber
asked.

"In April."

"Want me to get you on the Yard as an apprentice
then? They start boys at fifteen. You'd be making two
dollars a day in a year's time."

"Two dollars a day? Gee, Uncle George!"

"That's what Roland's going to do. Of course he won't
be fifteen until a year from June. But by starting then
he'll be well up the ladder by the time he's twenty."

"But he can live at home," Frankie said. "Hal
couldn't. I wouldn't want Hal to leave home at fifteen."

"Why, he could stay with us," Hattie said. "Couldn't
he, George? And ride back and forth with you? Of
course he could! And I'd do for him just as I do for
Roly."

"I know you would, Hattie, but —"

"I think Hal will go through the Academy," said
Vinnie quietly. "I think he'll graduate . . . There, the
sink's clear now if you want to wash. We're ready to
dish up."

She had just finished the gravy. Frankie hurried
through the sinkroom with the venison and the crackly
brown potatoes which sizzled in its juice. Behind her

the men took turns splashing in the basins, drinking from dippers, drying on the roller towel, and rattling combs in the tin case below the small mirror beside the cupboard door. Hattie was seasoning the squash she had put through the colander. Vinnie and Frankie were placing the turkey at one end of the table, the venison at the other, and heaping deep dishes with hot vegetables. Marcy filled the last goblet.

Off came the aprons.

"You sit here, George. And Marcy between the boys. There, I guess we're all —"

And there they were in their places — all who had ever lived here save one — at a laden table which nearly filled the small room. Only its walls and windows stood between them and the cold, gray sky, the frozen ground, the bare hardwood trees, the stiff evergreens, and Nature which had withdrawn from them as woods mothers do from their children, ceased to speak, turned a deaf ear, and gone about her secret, personal business. Yet they were sheltered, warm, together, and about to be royally fed, the men in clean, dark shirts with wet, slicked-back hair, the women and Marcy in bright dresses the women had made from remnants off a pedlar's cart, or from a bolt of new cloth, or from other dresses someone had passed down to them — garnet cashmere, green silk, pink batiste, blue serge, brown plaid jumper over a brown wool guimpe.

They looked at one another in sudden silence.

Frankie wished she could ask someone to say grace, as it had always been said at her grandfather's house where she grew up, not only at Thanksgiving but before every meal her grandfather ate. She imagined her mother was saying it now, at Lula's. But it was never said here.

George cleared his throat.

"They had food some'at like this at the first Thanksgiving," he said. "Only their meat was all wild. Wild turkeys, there was then. And they had deer meat, I don't doubt. Come a long way, they had, to be their own masters. Had a tough winter ahead. No floors in their houses, I guess; no window glass; maybe no chimneys to take off the smoke. Still they figgered they'd started something, and so they had. So they had. And we've managed to car' it on so we're fixed about as good as anybody could ask. Prob'ly we're the best off people in the world, here in America. Hattie, you like the dark best, don't ye? Pass Hattie's plate down to Verd, now, for a slice of Hal's deer. Vinnie, you want a piece off the breast?"

"Small," Vinnie answered, "and a big spoonful of Frankie's stuffing. Yes, we've gone a long way since the days of the Pilgrims. Gained our independence, established a sound government, laid out towns and built cities from sea to sea. None of it was easy and none of it was safe. But it's been worth the work and the risk. The process has made us strong, and we'll stay a strong people as long as we keep on working toward what we want to have and what we want to be, and never get afraid to risk what we have for the sake of what we want for the future."

"And keep our faith in God and live according to it," said Frankie. "Somebody wrote, 'In His will is our peace.' I often think of that."

"Dante," said Vinnie. "You'll be reading Dante some day, Hal, and so will Marcy. But you'll probably read Milton first. It's quite a thing to live in a country where a boy — or a girl either — can get all the education he's bound to have. You don't need to belong to a certain social class to get an education. You don't even need a lot of money. You can earn your own way, if you're of a mind to."

"That kind of education you're talking about isn't everything," said George Webber. "We've come to a place where we have to have a lot of people who understand machinery. Know how to build it, how to run it, how to repair it."

"That's so," Verd agreed. "Of course we've been getting there for some time. With trains, and the telegraph, and Uncle Joe Brown setting up steam shovels all over the country and showing crews how to run them. And now there's the telephone — they're even getting them in around here — and automobiles and airships —"

"Oh, you've got no idea how fast machinery is coming in everywhere," George Webber said. "And it's only a drop in the bucket to what it's going to be. The engine and electricity — why, time's coming when they'll take us wherever we want to go in half the time it takes now, and light and heat our houses and keep our milk and butter cold and run our tools. Oh, I tell you, the time's coming when a master mechanic or a master electrician will make more money than doctors and lawyers do now, maybe without working more than eight hours a day five days a week."

"We'll still need doctors and lawyers," said Vinnie.

"And ministers," said Frankie. "And teachers. People to make and keep us good. Because we have to run this country, and only good people can make and keep a good country."

"Good and wise," said Vinnie. "And brave."

"Way I look at it," said George, "people are going to be hard put to keep ahead of these machines, and if they don't machines are going to be running the people and the country too. Now I've got a mowing machine and I can run it; I can fix it if it gets loose; it saves me a lot of time. But I can still swing a scythe too, to clip out around a tree, along walls, and under fences. Time ever comes that a man don't know how to mow by hand, or don't have the strength to, he's going to have a pretty ragged looking field. And if he gets a mowing machine that only a master mechanic understands and it breaks down, cattle will starve to death. Get as many machines as you say, can't be a master mechanic for every one of 'em, onless everybody's a master mechanic. If they are, a lot of other work is bound to be slighted, even if everybody puts in a full day six days a week. And I will say, George, that people willing to set around all but eight hours of five days a week ain't going to be the same kind that've made this country what 'tis today."

Marcy had not often heard her grandfather say so many words without stopping.

"Now what do you suppose Marcy is making of all this?" asked Hattie. "Little pitchers have big ears, you know."

And suddenly everyone was refusing another helping, Hal and Roland were out racing around the barn to get back their appetites, the men were talking about the election, Frankie and Hattie were taking away the plates and filling the coffee and tea cups, Vinnie was in the shedroom cutting the pies into sections for Marcy to carry to the table.

"Will it be like they said, Auntie?" asked Marcy. "People will stop working and machines will run the people and there won't be any doctors and lawyers and ministers and teachers?"

"It might if people let it," Vinnie answered. "You're one of the people. Are you going to let it? What are *you* going to be when you grow up?"

"I thought I'd write books," Marcy said gravely. "But maybe I'd better be a teacher. To be sure there is at least one."

"Be both," said Vinnie. "Write your books on weekends. There will always be work — *important* work — for every single person to do, every day of the week, if only he is determined to find it and do it. It's *doing* that makes life good, and a country great. What needs to be done changes. Your grandfather didn't have to do what the Pilgrims did for him. We don't have to do what he has done for us. But we have to do our own part in our own time."

They finished their dinner and the men talked while the women put away the food and did the dishes. The gray light in the sky was growing dimmer and Frankie lit a lamp and set it in the center of the table. It turned the air rosy, and a rosy streak appeared along the horizon above the marshes as if the warmth and brightness of the kitchen had run out and tossed Nature some delicious scraps from its apron as a thank offering for the past and a gesture of hope for the future.

Marcy went into her grandfather's room and knelt by his bed.

"Thank you, God," she whispered, "for the Pilgrims and America and Grandpa and everybody here and Elder Knight and Teacher and the dinner, and help me work hard and do my part, and never let me be run by a machine. For Jesus' sake, amen."

DECEMBER

DECEMBER is Christmas.

The first rising of the December sun brings with it a gleam of wonder, narrow, distant, but clearly discernible, glowing like mother-of-pearl. The farmer is aware of it as soon as he opens his door to go toward the barn, the housewife when she comes shivering into the kitchen and glances out the east window, the child at the lifting of his eyelids from sleep.

With each setting of the sun, and each rising and setting of the moon and stars in the dark sky, the wonder grows. It is not so much in color as in absence of color, less in sound than in absence of sound, not at all in fragrance but in absence of fragrance; that is, of earthly color, sound, and fragrance. Each day there seems less of all that has been familiar in the earlier months of the year, and more that is new though not strange. Gradually the world becomes quite another place, suffused by gentle radiance, cupped in innocence and infinite wisdom, carried aloft by unseen winds which bear it closer and closer to the Source of all wonder.

Why are human beings not frightened by the transformation? Why are they not reluctant to be transported? We do not speak now of those who are in such dark places that they do not see or feel what is happening, but of the farmer, the housewife, the child, and all who are keenly aware of it from the beginning, from that first pearly gleam at the first rising of the December sun. Why do they go so eagerly, though on tiptoe, to meet it, turn up their faces to it, open their arms to it, wait to be caught up in it as in their natural home, as by their dearest beloved? There is something written here to strengthen man's self-respect, if he can read the script.

God so loved the world that He gave His only begotten Son . . .

Would He have given Him to the world had He not *known* that there were those already there and many more to come who longed for Him, could recognize Him, would cherish Him and follow Him?

This year there was the morning when Frankie, Hal, and Marcy climbed into Verd's pung at daybreak, and rode with him to the Junction to take the train to Portsmouth. The snow was so cold that the runners squeaked as they moved and Bess's flying feet threw out icy snowballs. Frankie had put hot beach rocks on the floor and brought hot potatoes to hold in their laps, but the air was so cold that it stung Marcy's nose until she hid it in her father's sleeve; but she could not bear to hide her eyes, for there was the moon, a silver crescent, swinging ahead of them in the pale sky. The bells on the shafts rang out sharply against the frost, and the white foam on the fence rails were turning pink.

The Junction is so called because not long ago it was a railroad center where the Eastern and Western Divisions of the Boston and Maine came together, there were great sheds to house the fuel for the wood-burning engines, there was a restaurant known far and wide for its Berwick sponge cake, and Mose Bennett kept a store and a post office. But now the Eastern and Western Divisions meet farther down the line toward Portland, the engines burn coal, the sheds and the restaurant have been razed, the mailman brings winter letters in his sleigh to the farms, the store is closed, Mose Bennett is dead, and Mose's son works at the shoeshop in the village. He walks to the shop and carries a lantern in winter when it is dark in the woods at both ends of his work day.

Marcy saw the glint of light at the tree line as Bess whirled into the station yard.

"What's that?" she asked. "That light in the woods?"

"That's Charlie Bennett going to work. He always goes down the Old Track," her father answered. "I'd give him a ride but he says Bess goes too fast for him. Says he don't like to run sitting down. Says the only time he rode with me he could have set a hen on his coattails and never lost an egg."

Hal laughed in the back seat of the pung. Hal does not often laugh aloud.

Verd said to Frankie, "You'll need some money. I think I can get some across the road. Jim's owed me for painting his buggy for some time, but I guess he'll want to pay up before Christmas." He pulled out his watch. "Ten minutes till train's due. You go in where it's warm."

In the little station a fire crackled in the chunk stove, reddening the cover. The narrow boards of the floor had been oiled. The wood settees had been varnished. The only sound was the clicking of the telegraph. They sat listening to it.

"If Papa can't get the money, can you buy our tickets?" Marcy whispered.

"No, but he will get it. Your father will tell Jim we are waiting for it to go to Portsmouth with. Jim is honest. He will pay what he owes."

"What if the train comes before Papa does?"

"It won't."

Verd came in and gave Frankie money. He gave Marcy a dollar and she put it in the crocheted pocket buttoned to the belt of her coat. He asked Hal if he needed money and Hal said no, he had his own. Verd's collar was turned up and the earmuffs of his fur cap were turned down. His face was red from the cold. He was smiling and his teeth looked very white.

"Not a cloud in the sky," he said. "Good day for your trip. I'll get your tickets."

He went to the high gate in the wall. Through the gate they could see the station agent blow out his lamp, spin around on his chair, take off his green eyeshade, and come to meet Verd.

"Morning, Herb."

"Morning, Verd."

"Three to Portsmouth. One's under twelve."

"Round trip?"

"No. They're coming back by way of Dover on the electrics."

Drawers opened and closed. Money was pushed under the gate. Tickets and money came back.

"Train 'bout on time, Herb?"

"Ought to be coming round the bend any minute now."

"Better head my horse towards the village then. She's skittish."

"Always said you ought to made a racer out of her."

The words were like bright round beads strung on the chain of the clicking telegraph in the silent room with the oiled floor and the varnished settees.

Verd came back and gave Frankie the tickets. He stood putting on his mittens, smiling down at the three.

"What do you think — going to wait where it's warm or go out on the platform and watch her come in?"

They went out with him. He touched Marcy's chin, clapped Hal on the shoulder, looked at Frankie in her black caracul coat and muff, with a bit of her garnet cashmere dress showing where the skirt of the coat parted in the wind, her black velvet hat held on by garnet-headed pins thrust through her dark hair and by a long scarf of golden gauze.

"Well," he said, "you've got a great day for it. I'll meet the five o'clock car in the Square."

He sprang into the pung, pulled up after him the iron weight to which Bess was tied, and a minute later had jingled away among the dark willows of Old Swamps.

The three were alone with the sun coming up and setting the pure white world aglisten. The square little station behind them was such a house as the Three Bears or the Seven Dwarfs might have gone out from in the forest. Between it and the frozen river ran two black lines equidistant from each other as far as the eye could see in both directions. Nothing moved and there was no sound. But in the black lines there was a pulsing as in the wrist even when no finger touches it.

And soon there was sound, a puffing, a rumble, a high, long, sweet whistle, *"Too-o-o-o, too-o-o-o; too-too."* Around the bend of the river, out of the dark trees into the glistening world, along the black lines came the lacy black triangle of the cowcatcher, the rolling black iron wheels, the smokestack tossing dark balloons with flecks of fire in them against the blue sky, the brass bell rocking and clanging.

Marcy reached for her mother's hand.

She came straight toward them, nearer and nearer, and the wind she made pushed Marcy backward at the same time that the great wheels wove a spell which drew Marcy toward them. The noise of bell and iron on iron and screeching brake was deafening.

Then she stopped, and everything was still again. From an open window below the smokestack an old man with a beard, wearing a bright blue cap and a coat with brass buttons, smiled down at Marcy.

"Well, well, little lady! Where shall I take you this bright morning? To the North Pole?"

"All aboard!" a younger man in darker blue with

brass buttons was calling as he swung down high steps. "All-l aboard here—"

Frankie hurried Marcy along the icy platform, past a little red car heaped with black coal where still another man in a blue coat was shoveling but stopped shoveling to wave at them. The young man reached out for Marcy, picked her up and stood her on the top step saying, "All the princesses ride in my coach," and turned to put his hand under Frankie's elbow.

"Take seats at this end near the stove," he said. "Upper end is still cold. Set on a spur track all night, and ten below when we left Portland."

Their seats were of gold with red velvet cushions, and faced each other as the seats in royal coaches always do. A lady in furs and a gentleman in a brown derby hat sat near by. Perhaps they were a queen and a king. Several men sat alone, some of them reading newspapers. Perhaps they were footmen. There was no other child but Marcy.

The train began to move.

"I didn't have time to answer the nice old man," Marcy whispered. "He doesn't know where we want to go."

"He is the engineer. The man who was shoveling coal is the fireman. The one who lifted you in is the conductor. The conductor is coming now to take our tickets. The tickets say where we want to go."

But Marcy did not think tickets could speak as plainly as she could. She summoned her courage, and when the conductor came she said aloud:

[251]

"Please, sir, tell the engineer we want to go to Portsmouth. If it — isn't out of his way."

"I will tell the fireman," said the conductor, bowing. "He will tell the engineer. At once. Yes, ma'am."

They were flying now through the glistening fields.

The conductor opened the glass door at the end of the coach and stepped out on the platform. The fireman looked out of a little window beyond the coal, and then turned and spoke to someone behind him. When he turned back he tossed a small package across the coal. The conductor caught it and brought it to Marcy.

"He says he will be glad to take you to Portsmouth on our way to the North Pole. And he sent you this which he brought back from his last trip up there."

It was a small gold box with white paper lace inside. Under the lace there were four cookies shaped like snowflakes. Each cookie was two cookies with cream candy between. One was chocolate with white cream. One was white with pink cream. One was crusted with sugar crystals. One had yellow frosting. There was a shiny white card lettered in gold, "Compliments of the Sunshine Biscuit Co."

"Are you going to eat them, Marcy?" Hal asked.

Her heart stopped beating. If one was eaten, it would be gone forever. There would be an empty place in the gold box which had come to her from the bearded old man with the twinkling eyes, the North Pole, and the Sunshine Biscuit Company . . . But there had been no present for Hal. Nobody had even spoken to him.

She took off the cover and turned back the lace.

"You first," Hal said. "It's yours."

A lump began rising in Marcy's throat. She knew she could not swallow.

"She loves so to keep things, Hal," Frankie said. "You can't be hungry yet. You had a good breakfast. We'll get something to eat in Portsmouth. Or Dover."

"Oh, keep it, Marcy, if you want to, till it turns to dust. Let's watch for the Webber place and the Bannister place. Aunt Hattie might be out feeding the hens. Aunt Vinnie might be hanging out clothes."

Rushing through the glistening new world, past little fences around little white houses and little red barns, now and then they saw little figures moving about or riding in little sleighs behind little horses. Perhaps one of the little houses was Hattie's, or one of the little figures Vinnie.

"We're coming into Kittery Depot," said the conductor. "When we stop, young feller, you want to come up front and ride into Portsmouth in the cab?"

"With the engineer?" Hal exclaimed. "You bet! Gee!"

As soon as the train stopped, Hal went up the aisle with his mackinaw unbuttoned to show his blue shirt and with his knitted cap pulled low over his eyes as if it were visored. The glass door closed behind him. Marcy watched him balance on the side of the coal car as on a tightrope and disappear into the cab. The smoke came out of the stack blacker than ever.

"Will the engineer let Hal drive the train?" asked Marcy.

"Maybe," said Frankie dreamily. Of course he wouldn't. But would he — today?

Marcy thought Hal drove the train very well. It stayed right on the tracks. She took the cover off the gold box and touched the crystal-crusted cookie with the tip of one finger. It felt sharp.

"See the harbor, Marcy," said Frankie. "There's the Navy Yard where Uncle George works."

They were on a high bridge over the Piscataqua River, the blue sky and blue water on both sides of them. Dories, fishing boats, cargo boats and a ferry sat on the water like brown and white ducks and ducklings, those at the shoreline frozen in. The low yellow buildings of the Navy Yard covered the island at the mouth of the river and beyond them a tall ship like a white eagle with wings spread was moving out into the open sea. Ahead of the engine were the red brick walls and the black chimney pots of the city of Portsmouth.

The train came to a stop. The people who had been together on it separated and went out into the narrow streets, up the hill to cobblestoned Market Square and the stores which surrounded it. Hal had ridden with the engineer. Marcy had her cookies from the North Pole. Frankie had money in her beaded bag.

Every door had a green wreath tied with a bow of red ribbon. In a few windows there were Christmas trees hung with many colored balls and silver cones and tiny golden trumpets. One window had nothing in it but a great framed picture of Washington's Christmas at Valley Forge. Hal looked at that for a long time, and kept going back to look at it. All the other windows were filled with wonderful things to look at. Wherever they went inside there were more wonderful things still, and when Frankie bought a pillowtop for Vinnie, with skeins of floss to embroider the pattern printed on it, the money she gave the saleslady was put into a little wooden box which was snapped onto a track and went zinging up to the ceiling and down the whole length of the store to a balcony where a girl with red hair took out the bill and put in some coins and sent the box zinging back to the saleslady and Frankie.

They were outside and it was very cold. The horses hitched to the granite posts were blanketed, and the chimes were playing in the church tower.

Sometime while the sun was high they rode on a ferryboat across the river to where an electric car, painted yellow, came into Kittery on its trolley wire much as the little wooden box had traveled to the balcony and back. Frankie and Hal and Marcy got into it and went zinging through snowy woods and fields to Dover. Here, too, were the wreaths, the little trees with bright balls, the wonderful things in windows and on counters, the blanketed horses, and the chimes. It must be that they were not far from anywhere. Ride in any direction and you would come to them.

Somewhere they sat at a table covered with a white cloth and ate steaming oyster stew. Somewhere Marcy was alone with Hal and bought a great blue vase for her mother; it was blue but it was green and purple and garnet, too, changing magically from one color to another. Somewhere she was with her mother and bought socks for her father, grandfather, and Hal, a set of three bluebird pins for her Aunt Vinnie and a new moon

pin for her Aunt Lula, smaller vases for her grandmother, her Aunt Hattie and her teacher. She had just
enough money left from her dollar to buy what she had
wanted most to buy, except the blue vase: a coral
bracelet for Bernice.

Somewhere they found an ice cream parlor and sat in
chairs with heart-shaped backs to have ice cream sodas.
Marcy's was pink; strawberry. Frankie's was brown;
sarsaparilla. Hal's was almost black; chocolate. The
presents they had bought were heaped around their feet,
and the chimes were playing, and all the people were
talking and smiling. They didn't smile only at people
they knew. They smiled at everybody, especially at
children. They smiled at Marcy and Marcy smiled back.

She thought, "I love you. I want to take you home
with me."

When they got off the electric car in the village square
it was growing dark and the conductor held his red
lantern to light them down the steps.

"Here you are," he said to Verd. "Got 'em all
back to you safe and sound. Leave it to the old P., D.,
and Y."

"Much obliged," Verd said, "but I probably won't
chance it again for another year."

They both laughed.

"Wish you merry Christmas, Mr. Conductor," said
Marcy boldly.

"Well, God love ye, wish you the same."

The electric zinged on toward Salmon Falls. Verd put
the packages under the pung seat, they all climbed in,
and Bess set off full tilt toward home. The farther they

went the darker it grew, and the brighter the lamplight
was in the windows of each house they passed.

"Must have seen and heard and done a lot today,"
Verd said. "What did you think was the best of it all?"

"Oh, the sunshine on the river and the boats in the
harbor," Frankie answered. "And the music. The
chimes."

"The engine," said Hal. "I rode in it with the engineer. And a picture they had in a Portsmouth window.
Christmas at Valley Forge."

"What do you say, Marcy?"

She thought of the royal coach, the golden box of
cookies, the wreaths, the Christmas trees, the zinging
wooden box, the zinging electrics, the oyster stew, the
strawberry soda, the dolls and toys, the vases and pins
and bracelets.

But she said, "The people. All the smiling people with
love in their eyes."

There were the days the mailman left postcards and
packages stamped "Boston" and "Lawrence" and
"Eliot." Frankie put the packages in the sitting-room
cupboard but the postcards were passed from hand to
hand many times before being tucked into the album.
There were glazed cards and frosted cards, pictures of
Santa with his pack, a mother cat with a holly-trimmed
basket of kittens, the Wise Men following the Star, and
the Baby in the manger. One of Frankie's was from a
woman she had gone to school with when they were little
girls. They have not seen each other for years but they
write when they can. The card had a picture of two little
girls running through the snow, and a verse:

No gift to send,
Only love to share
With my old friend —
A friendship rare.

There were the evenings Frankie sewed, and helped Marcy with her pincushions, needlebooks, and bookmarks, while George, Verd, and Hal packed a barrel for Annie, filling it with the vegetables she so enjoyed, protected with hay from the cold, a big piece of salt pork, a slab of home-cured bacon, and a slice of deer steak. Always before bedtime Verd brought up a basin of Strawberry Baldwins from the cellar, peeled them, and passed around quarters on the point of his jackknife.

There was the Sunday afternoon when Grace and Bernice came, and Frankie asked Verd to build a fire in the sitting-room stove so that the children could play in that room while she and Grace talked in the kitchen.

As soon as the women were alone, Grace took Larkin catalogues, record books, and order pads from her bag, and Frankie brought hers, along with ink bottle and pens. When these were spread out, they covered the table, and the women began eagerly to check each other's figures. Grace's total was higher than Frankie's because she had had a horse to take her over many roads where people lived who gave her orders, but Grace had two sons to earn premiums for, while Frankie had only one. And Frankie had been helped by orders Vinnie, Hattie, and Annie had given her. They rejoiced together that not only had each sold enough to get the Big Doll, but Frankie could get a set of drafting tools for Hal,

and Grace could get a catcher's mitt and mask for Clyde,
a new wheel and a bell for Leslie's bicycle.

They wrote the orders for the boys' gifts quickly, but
selection among the dolls was a happy task they lingered
over, reading the descriptions aloud in low voices, studying the pictures of perfect little wax faces, dimpled
hands, shod feet, and pastel silk dresses.

"Look at the length of this one's eyelashes."

"Oh, Grace, what would we have thought to have a
doll like that when we were their age?"

"There, dear, what we didn't know of didn't hurt us.
We thought my Adelaide was the handsomest thing we
ever —"

"Sh-h-h!"

Frankie had heard Marcy's voice raised in the next
room.

"You know what? We don't *have* to write letters to
him! We could *talk* to him right here because right
behind that tin that the stove funnel goes through there's
a fireplace. I always used to wish they didn't have to set
up the stove before Christmas, and I never thought
until now — the fireplace is *there* just the same and I
guess he can hear through a little old piece of tin!"

" 'Course he can," Bernice agreed. "You talk to him
first."

"All right. We'll have to talk *loud.* Because of the
tin. Besides, he's so old he may be getting a little mite
deaf."

"Listen, Grace. They're going to tell Santa Claus what
they want."

Frankie was smiling, both in amusement and in pride.

Marcy had not been long in school when older children had told her there was no Santa Claus. It pleased Frankie that Marcy was not passing on any such disillusionment to Bernice, who had not yet been to school. It also amused her that Marcy was making sure her histrionic effort would not be wasted.

"Hello, up there, Santa Claus!" shouted Marcy. "I have been as good as usual, and I hope you will bring me a new doll. If possible I would like to have a bed for her and Margery to sleep in. Hal would like a compass to use when he takes geometry. I hope you know what kind of compass he means. It is not the kind you carry in your pocket to help you find your way when you are lost. We would also like oranges and sheep's-foot nuts. I hope this isn't asking too much. Thank you, Santa Claus, and merry Christmas! . . . Now it's your turn, Bernice. Get right in close, back of the stove, and *talk loud!*"

"Hello, Santa Claus," piped Bernice. "I think I have been good. Please bring me a new doll, and — and picture books, and a new album to put my postcards in, and Christmas candy. Clyde wants a new mitt and Leslie broke the front wheel of his bicycle. If you can only bring one thing for me, what I want the most is a new doll with — with brown hair. Thank you, Santa Claus."

"Did you hear her, Santa Claus?" bawled Marcy. "She said *a doll with brown hair*. I'd rather have a doll with yellow hair like hers. She wants brown hair and I want yellow hair, Santa!"

"Well, I guess that settles the hair," Frankie murmured.

Grace's face was all lighted up. She put a hand over Frankie's.

"Oh, am I thankful, dear!" she whispered. "I held my breath. You see, Will's niece told Bernice when they came on a visit last summer that there isn't any Santa Claus. Bernice felt awful bad at the time, but she hasn't said anything about it since. I was so afraid she'd tell Marcy."

There was the Saturday after a three-day storm when George and Hal drove to the beach for a cartload of seaweed to be used as fertilizer in the potato hills next spring, and Hal brought back a pailful of shells of many shapes and sizes which he and his mother and Marcy decorated with red and gold paint Verd brought home from the shop. Hal chipped a small hole in each shell and Frankie threaded them with red twine for hanging on the tree, which had not yet been brought from the woods. As they worked, Hal tried to tell them about the sight and the sound of December surf.

"It's nothing like the summer ocean. I don't know words that would describe it. I wish I'd taken your camera."

"I guess a camera couldn't see all of it. Maybe a painting — but we'd still have to imagine the sound. Or music, some great piece of music — but then we'd have to imagine the color. And the cold. You know, the poorest people are the people who don't have imagination. Even if you don't have all you want to eat, or felt boots, or a tight roof over your head — if you just have imagination —''

That night after Marcy went to bed she practised imagining. She imagined that her bed was a sled on which she lay while her father pulled it along the cobblestone street of a city like Portsmouth. It was snowing. She could feel the little prickles of snowflakes on her face. She looked about her at the ribboned wreaths on the doors, at the dolls in the windows, at the ships in the harbor, the engines puffing smoke, and the zinging electrics. It grew dark and very cold. She snuggled deeper into the comforters. At last they stopped under a tall gaslight and her mother began to sing. Her mother's strong clear, sweet voice ran up the lamppost, spread out from the top in bright rays of light, and unfurled over the city like a shining banner . . . *O little town of Bethlehem . . . Silent night, holy night . . .*

Her father had taken off his hat, stood bareheaded in the sifting snow. The wreathed doors opened and smiling people came running out. Smiling people came off the ships and out of the trains and down the steps of the electrics, and made a smiling circle around them. At the end of the singing they tossed gold pieces into Verd's hat until it spilled over and the bright coins sprinkled, tinkling, on the ice.

''Now we shall have wood for a fire and matches to light it,'' said Verd. ''We shall have good bread to eat, and maybe oranges for Christmas.''

''Why?'' Marcy asked sleepily. ''Why do they give us these things?''

''Because they love us,'' Frankie answered. ''Because

this is a holy time. Because they are good and kind . . ."

"And because," Verd added, "of the way your mother sings."

There was the night of the Christmas Party at school. For the first time in her life Marcy left home after supper, sitting between Verd and Frankie in the cutter, buried to her chin in the buffalo robe. She saw the streak of light from the lantern hung on the corner of the dashboard. She saw the dark, and she saw the stars. She heard the sleighbells. She felt the curves of the road, the planks of White's Marsh bridge, the pitch of Nason's hill. Then she came up out of the robe and saw beyond the horse's head the lighted windows of the schoolhouse, a dozen horses and sleighs hitched to the schoolyard fence.

The schoolhouse door was closed. When they opened it and stepped inside, the little room was full of people and lantern light and the smell of spruce and kerosene. It buzzed with voices. It rocked with footsteps. And the great tree, hung all over with books and toys and packages and red cheesecloth bags, was like a happy mother beaming on a great brood of noisy children bringing more and more packages to put in her hands, lay at her feet, and pin in her hair.

Teacher in a red velvet dress, at a desk streaming evergreen, tapped her bell.

"Santa Claus is coming soon," she promised. "All take seats, please. The pupils in front. Parents in back. We have prepared a program we hope you will enjoy."

"Marcy." It was Bernice. "Marcy — can I sit with you?"

Marcy moved over. The seat was very narrow. They clung together to stay on it, and because they were so glad they were both there.

"The December Song," announced Teacher. "By our youngest pupil, Marcia Hasty."

It was terrifying to be first, to leave Bernice and stand alone on the platform beside the tree, to see all the dark heads bobbing against the lantern light, to open her mouth and let out the first note. It might so easily be the wrong note. It so often was the wrong note.

"Jesus, help me," Marcy prayed.

> *Oh, December, how we love you, and the many joys you bring*
> *'Tis the time of dear old Santa, when the merry, merry sleighbells ring.*
> *Jingle, jingle through the frosty air, folks are traveling here and there,*
> *Laughing, singing, happiness to spare, jingle, jingle, jingle everywhere.*
> *Tiny stockings hanging in a row; children sleeping, lights are burning low,*
> *Santa comes with many gifts and toys for all good little girls and boys,*

Marcy's eyes sought her mother's face. Frankie nodded and smiled. Most of the notes must have been almost right.

She ran back to her seat. Bernice's arm was waiting. They hugged each other fiercely.

It was wonderful to have been first.

"I put a present on the tree for you," whispered Bernice.

"I put one on for you, too," Marcy whispered back.

The other pupils recited and sang and did a little play with three big boys dressed as the Wise Men and a big girl as Mary holding a big doll. The grown-ups listened. The children watched the tree and the soft shadows, smelled the spruce, and thought about Jesus. This was Bethlehem and they knew He was about to be born.

The last number on the program was the singing of "Jingle Bells," and Teacher asked everyone to join in. Marcy could hear her mother's voice above all the rest, strong and gay and sweet.

. . . Bells on bobtail ring, making spirits bright,
What fun it is to ride and sing a sleighing song tonight!

Jingle-jingle-jingle . . . HO-HO-HO . . . WHOA, DONDER . . . WHOA, BLITZEN . . .

"Well, well, *well!* Here you are, then! Merry Christmas, young folks, old folks, and folks in the middle! By zounds, what a handsome tree! Who do you suppose these presents are for? Just a minute till I wipe off my glasses —"

Red suit, red stocking-leg cap, white beard, twinkling eyes, fat stomach, high black boots . . . It was Hal. It was not Hal. It was Christmas very close now. Not close enough to touch. But very close.

The warm, booming voice was reading names. The gloved hands below the white fur cuffs were passing out gifts.

"Albra! Albra! Where is Albra?... Here's a pretty book for you, Lucy . . . Mar — Marcy — *Hasty!* Ho, HO, HO, so you're Marcy Hasty, are you?"

"Yes, I am," answered Marcy pertly. "I should think you'd know me, Santa Claus!"

"Ho, ho, yes, indeed. I know all you children. But once in a while I forget a name for a minute. Old man, remember."

Marcy's gift was a picture of a little girl in a sunbonnet. It had a scalloped gold frame and a gold chain to hang by. On the cardboard back was written, "Marcy Hasty. Merry Christmas from Teacher."

"You'll get a present from her as soon as you come to school," Marcy told Bernice. "She always puts something for every one of us on the tree. But I never thought I'd get a picture. I never had a picture of my own before."

There was a red cheesecloth bag with a popcorn ball in it, and peanuts and peppermint sticks, for every person in the room; and some left over to be sent to small children who had not come.

"Bernice! Bernice Dorr! Now where's that little Bernice?"

"You get it, Marcy," Bernice whispered, sliding low in her seat.

"I'll take it for her, Santa! Here. I got it for you the day I rode on the train."

"Where's mine for you?"

"He just hasn't come to it yet."

"I'm going to wait till you get yours."

That was how it happened that at the very end, when

Santa had gone and boys were pawing through the branches piled around the trunk of the tree to be sure nothing more was hidden there, and mothers were coming with coats and leggings, and some of the lanterns were beginning to sputter because the oil was low, Bernice and Marcy pulled the red ribbons from two little white boxes and took off the covers. A card in one said, in printed letters, "Merry Christmas to Bernice from Marcy." A card in the other said in Grace's handwriting, "To Marcy with love, from Bernice." And under each card was a coral bracelet.

Now Christmas was rising to a crescendo.

There was the day Mr. Bannister brought Vinnie home, and had to leave right away because he was going to travel on a train all that night and all the next day and all the next night to be a Christmas present to his sister in Florida.

When he had gone, and Vinnie had taken off her hat and cape and sat down in her rocking chair by the back window, it was as if she had never been away. The fire crackled and the teakettle sang and when Hal brought in the mail the usual black type and blacker headlines of the weekly *Independent* were surrounded by dark green leaves and bright red berries, and the rays from the Star in the corner swept the whole page.

That night they made long strings of popcorn and cranberries.

The next day — the morning of the day before Christmas — Vinnie said as soon as Frankie came downstairs:

"Now Verd and I have planned it all out. He and Hal are going up on the mountain this afternoon to get a tree he's taken a notion to up there. So why don't you and Marcy ride along with them to Clarence's and take your presents to your mother and Lula? I'll cut some nice slices off that ham I brought, so if your mother's baked some bread you can have some good sandwiches for your dinner, all of you. Verd says he'll come back for you after dark. They'll bring the tree down first, and Hal and I figure to have it decorated before you get home.''

Marcy rode down the lane and down the hill and over Warren's bridge between Verd and Frankie on the seat of the woodsled, with Old Bell swishing her tail before them. Hal stood in the back. Everything was blue above and white below except for the red barns and the dark trees.

At Emerys', Frankie's Aunt Em was taking a handful of bright cards from the mailbox.

She pushed back her shawl from her cheek, and smiled, and said, ''Well, now, where you folks off to?''

''Up to Lula's to spend the day,'' Frankie called back. ''That is, Marcy and I are. Verd and Hal are going after the Christmas tree. What are you going to do tomorrow, Aunt Em?''

''Do! I guess there'll be enough to do! All of them that aren't here are coming for dinner and the tree in the afternoon, way they always do. Grace and her young ones, and Maude and hers. Georgie's got our tree set up, and Cathie'll be baking all day.''

''Oh, what a good time you'll have!''

''Wait a minute,'' Aunt Em called after them. ''I've got a card here from Nell. Let's see what she says. Oh —

says Than thinks to drive down this afternoon. Tell Louise he may be up there before he goes home.''

''I'll tell her,'' Frankie answered. ''I hope he will. I'd love to see him.''

Than Brooks is as near to a brother as she ever had, though he is her uncle. She grew up with her grandparents, and he is only thirteen years older than she. Hal is eight years older than Marcy.

They rode on the blue sleds into the dark and white woods. Above their heads there was a ribbon of blue to match the sleds. When they came to fields again, they were Clarence's fields, and Clarence's little white house with green blinds and a red, smoking chimney was waiting for them at the top of the bank wall.

Lula opened the door and ran to the steps in the bank wall to meet them; bareheaded, bare-armed, her hair — the color of the honey of Clarence's bees — pinned low on her slender neck, her eyes — blue as turquoises — laughing.

''I had a *feeling* you'd come! I told Mama —''

''Oh, Lula, you naughty girl! Get back inside before you get your death of cold.''

''Know what I'm making? A tapioca pudding with bananas and oranges!'' She drew Marcy into the circle of her arm, waving to the men with the other hand. ''You like tapioca pudding, Marcy? And Grammy's bread — if nobody makes you eat the crusts?''

They all went into the house, and Louise came out of the pantry, which was painted spruce-gum pink and had shelves filled with blue and white plates and platters and cups and saucers all alike. She was wiping floury hands on her apron, and her scalp showed pink through her fine, silvery hair, and her eyes crinkled at the corners.

"Well, my land sakes alive," she said gently, "what a surprise, Frank! But Lula did say this morning she had a feeling —"

They had a box of new wax crayons for Marcy and they found some old magazines with pictures of ladies and children in fancy old-fashioned clothes. While she colored by the window they cooked and talked and gave each other aprons and hankerchiefs with tatted edging and little bags of sachet to tuck under bed pillows and crocheted flowers sewn to safety pins to hold their collars together.

They ate their ham sandwiches and pudding and drank their tea — there was cambric tea for Marcy — and Marcy gave her grandmother the little vase which changed from rose color to gold and back again, and Lula the new moon pin. She had painted a Bible and a gold cross on a bit of purple satin ribbon for a bookmark for her grandmother, too.

Lula put the pin over the top button of her blue wrapper and said, "There, Marcy, now I'm all dressed up."

Louise laid the bookmark carefully in her Bible and said, "When the cinnamon roses bloom next summer I'll have something better than a milk pitcher to put them in, won't I?"

"Are you going to sing?" asked Marcy. They always did.

"Sing? We'll sing our hearts out," cried Lula. "I'll get the books. They're on the stairs."

They were singing "We Three Kings of Orient Are" when the door opened and Em's strong soprano and Than's deep bass swept in and joined them. Lula jumped up, hugged them both, took their wraps, and they went around the table and kissed everybody, but nobody stopped singing.

Than swung Marcy out of her chair, dropped into it himself, pulled her onto his knee, and threw an arm around Frankie, leaning over to see the words of the second verse on her book.

They sang "Joy to the World," and "O Come, All Ye Faithful," and "Deck the Halls," and "We Wish You a Merry Christmas," and "The First Noel," and It Came Upon the Midnight Clear," and "Hark, the Herald Angels Sing" — all the verses of every one and some of them over and over.

"Well, Louise, I've got to go," Than said suddenly. He kissed Marcy, set her on her feet, and rose. "It's many a mile to old North Berwick, and I've got twelve cows to milk before supper."

"Have a taste of my pudding before you go, Uncle Than," Lula said.

She dipped some into a saucer.

"Oh, give Em the taste," he said. "I'll take the dish."

He picked up the bowl and a spoon and stood in the middle of the kitchen, eating, rolling his eyes, licking his lips, a big, happy, brown-faced, hawk-nosed giant. Than Brooks is six feet, four inches tall.

"My stars and garters, Lula, that's the best pudding I ever ate!"

Clarence came in from the woods with a little fir balsam. Verd was right behind him. They took off their mittens and shook hands with Than and Em, stood talking with Than while the women put on their wraps.

"Oh, Em, I'm so glad you came with him. I wish you could get up here oftener."

"Well, any chance I get I take. When he said he was coming up, I said, 'Well, I'm going to drop everything and go with you. Best present I could have.'"

"Oh, it does us all a world of good to get together and sing."

"Now you have a nice day tomorrow."

"I'll be thinking of you — and old times —"

"Give our love to Nell."

Louise and Lula stood in the doorway as the others climbed into the two sleighs. The sun was just dropping behind the trees.

As Than pulled on the reins to start his horse, he said in his deep, carrying voice:

"Well, here 'tis again. Christmas Eve!"

And there it was. The snow all turned to pearl, the dark trees strung with pearls, the sky beginning to glow with such a radiance as never was on land or sea. And the stillness everywhere; the live, vibrant stillness of just before a great orchestra begins to play, or angels to sing.

Later in the evening Marcy stood alone looking at the Christmas tree in the parlor, where a fire burned in the little round stove. The tree was looped around from top to bottom with the popcorn and cranberry strings.

Hattie had sent three little red balls, like shiny apples encased in golden mesh, and Vinnie had brought two silver cones and four little golden trumpets. They all hung here now, among the seashells, and the lamplight picked them out, every one. But best of all was the gold star Vinnie had brought and Hal had fastened to the very point of the tree, almost touching the white ceiling.

"Is it almost too beautiful to believe?" they had asked her when she first saw it.

Marcy had thought about that, and then shaken her head.

"The more beautiful it is, the easier I can believe it."

Now her father came up behind her and put his hand on her shoulder.

"Want to see what I got for your mother, Marcy?"

"Oh, yes."

He took a little bottle of perfume from his pocket. He held it to the lamp and she could see the pale yellow perfume inside. She thought it was pretty but she thought it was very small.

"It's the kind she likes," he said. "I had to go to Dover to get it. I got her something else, too. But mind you don't tell her."

"Oh, I won't."

He took the lamp to light a dark place under the stairs. There was a wooden box with a domed cover and beside the box there was a horn.

"It's a graphophone," he said, low. "Like the one they have at Dorrs' that she likes to go to listen to. Only theirs is an Edison and this is a Columbia. There

[273]

are twelve cylinders for it. Six of them are hymns.''

"Oh, Papa! Now she can have music even — even when she's hoarse and can't sing.''

"Yes. Now she can have music all the time.''

Music all the time . . .

As Frankie kissed Marcy good-night and was turning out the light in the alcove at the head of the stairs, Marcy asked drowsily, "Do you go out to see the cattle kneel down in the stalls at midnight?''

"No, Marcy. "

"Why? Have you gone to sleep by then?''

"No. I'm in my room, kneeling too.''

"I think — that's nice. That's what I'll do, too — when I'm old enough to be awake.''

"Yes, dear.''

Frankie went down to the parlor where Hal had brought in his Flexible Flyer which he had painted blue and gold for Marcy. Verd was just bringing in the bed he had made and stained red for the golden-haired doll. It had a spring of chicken wire and a frame to hold curtains at the head. Frankie began making up the bed with small sheets and pillow, a small tufted comforter, and white Marseilles spread and curtains.

In the kitchen George was saying, as he lay on the couch and Vinnie rocked quietly by the back window looking out at the stars:

"Good to have you home again, Vinnie.''

"I'll be back to stay awhile, by February.''

"How's that?''

"Mr. Bannister is going to be married.'' She laughed softly. "On Valentine's Day!''

After a minute he cleared his throat and said, ''Some thought you might be going to marry him.''

She laughed a little again.

''There was never such a thought in *my* mind . . . No, I want to be here when the ice goes out.''

Later he sat up and felt for his slippers, looking over at her.

''Must say, you've give me all the Christmas present I need.''

''Likely you'll get other ones. I made you a pair of shirts.''

''Wool ones?''

''Yes.''

''They'll come in handy.''

Hal had gone up to bed, but he could not sleep. Lying on his side he could see the sky all bright with stars, and one brighter than any of the rest.

Frankie blew out the parlor light, and went upstairs carrying a hand lamp. Verd followed her. Their shadows moved with them along the wall.

In their chamber she turned down the bed. Even this room was warm tonight, for he had kept a fire in it all the evening. He put a last chunk into the stove and closed the drafts. She stood at the bureau unpinning her hair. It fell in heavy, purplish-black masses to her waist. He came up beside her.

''Merry Christmas,'' he said, and gave her the little bottle.

She held it for an instant in both hands and then put it against her cheek. Her eyes were like June pansies.

''Oh, Verd!'' she said. ''The kind I love best!''

The last light went out and the little white house, at other times moored so securely to its granite foundation, seemed to set off like a sleigh along a smooth, dark road leading straight to the Milky Way, with the red barn following closely.

The kitchen clock struck midnight, and Bell, Bess, and all the cattle were kneeling down.

Now it is the last night of the Old Year and we lie in the dark below a sloping ceiling, or sit before the open oven door by the light of a lamp with wick turned low, waiting for the midnight stroke which will usher in a new year. One after another the old years go; one after another the new years come. We have no way of knowing what changes each will bring, but we go forward with faith that God will never ask of us more than we are capable of, and that what we earn, what we deserve, we shall receive in the coming year and all the years ahead.